OUR WONDERFUL EYES

WHITTLESEY HOUSE
McGRAW-HILL BOOK COMPANY
NEW YORK LONDON TORONTO

OUR WONDERFUL EYES

by JOHN PERRY

pictures by JEANNE BENDICK

FOREWORD BY GEORGE WALD
PROFESSOR OF BIOLOGY, HARVARD UNIVERSITY

OUR WONDERFUL EYES

Library of Congress Catalog Card Number: 54-12681
Published by Whittlesey House
A division of the McGraw-Hill Book Company, Inc.
PRINTED IN THE UNITED STATES OF AMERICA

SIXTH PRINTING

FOREWORD

Vision is a large subject. From one aspect it might be thought to be a small one: it is but one of many senses, and the eye but one of many organs. Yet what a dominant role vision plays in human life. Most of what we do is guided by it, most of what we know is learned by means of it. Even the blind depend upon it vicariously; the world would be a vastly poorer place for them were it not for those who see. We are visual beyond all other creatures, unless it be certain birds. We see better than most other animals, and rely more upon vision and less upon other senses than most others.

Mr. Perry has given us an extraordinarily lively and informative introduction to the eye and vision in this little book. As a teacher, I admire its clarity and skill of presentation. As a scientist, I enjoy the ingenuity with which Mr. Perry leads the reader to explore the subject for himself in clear and simple experiments which go directly to the mark and require no special apparatus or skills. Sometimes nowadays, when experimenting tends to be left to professionals and is pursued with an increasingly complex armament of gadgets, one forgets an earlier art by which the simplest of means were employed to obtain direct answers to straightforward questions. In this direction Mr. Perry has done something more than provide an introduction to vision. He has given us an extensive demonstration of inductive thinking and the art of experiment, as such worth more than a dozen tracts on "the scientific method."

Vision and all its ways are wonderful. My long experience with it in the laboratory has only made me appreciate more keenly its effectiveness, its accuracy, its sensitivity, its perfection of design—indeed, more wonderful still, its capacity to compensate for and circumvent imperfections of design. This book will introduce you to many of its marvels. I hope that some of you may be impelled to pursue them further.

GEORGE WALD

Harvard University,
Cambridge, Massachusetts

CONTENTS

USING YOUR EYES

THIS BOOK is about your eyes and how you use them.

You use them every day, every waking minute. But you have some surprises coming in the chapters that follow and in the experiments we shall perform together. Few people know how much they see.

Eyes have always fascinated people. Of all the parts of the body, they seem most "alive." Eyes have been called "the windows of the soul" through which the "real person" looks out at the world.

When you look at someone, you look at his eyes.

Writers describe their characters by describing their eyes. The hero has a "level gaze," and he fixes the villain with a "steely glance." The guilty man will not meet his accuser's eyes. The heroine's eyes sparkle.

Actors use their eyes. People in the audience, even those sitting far back, are aware of the actor's eyes, even a flicker of his glance from one place to another. A skilled actor can call attention to an object just by looking at it.

Eyes play a part in everyday conversation. Eyes tell us whether we have someone's attention, whether he understands us, whether he is pleased by what we say.

This is why we sometimes raise our voices, or even shout, when we talk to a blind man. This annoys the blind person, who can hear as well as anyone. But it is difficult, at first, to talk with someone who does not look at us and respond to our words with his eyes.

No scientific instrument is as sensitive to light as your eye. In the dark, its sensitivity increases 100,000 times, and you can detect a faint glow, less than a thousandth as bright as a candle's flame. You can see in brilliant, blazing light, too, in light brighter than the radiance of a billion candles.

You can see tiny specks a few inches away, or the magnificence of a broad landscape.

You can see the moon, 240,000 miles away. You can see light from the stars, and the nearest of all the stars is 24,000,000,000,000 miles away!

Eyesight is the exploring sense. Without eyes, your world would seem much smaller. Your sense of touch extends no farther than your arm. You taste only what enters your mouth. Even the loudest noises can be heard only a few miles away, and most of what you hear is much closer. Strong odors are carried a little distance by the wind, but to smell a flower you hold it close to your nose.

Imagine taking a walk through the woods in springtime, blindfolded. You smell the forest smells, a lovely fragrance—but you can recognize few details by smell. You feel the springy turf underfoot and hear the wind rustling through the trees and bushes.

The sun is warm on your face. But if the warmth vanishes you cannot tell whether you are in the shadow of a cloud or of a tree. You hear the cardinals and chickadees, but you do not know that buzzards and a bald eagle are circling overhead.

You have no way of knowing that the green forest is carpeted with mandrake, trillium, violets, and other spring flowers, that a swallowtail butterfly is spreading its new wings on a bush nearby. You cannot touch, taste, smell or even hear the green heron fishing by the riverbank.

Take off the blindfold and the world appears. Within the range of your vision are millions upon millions of leaves. Yet your eyes detect a tiny flicker of motion in a tree, and you see a goldfinch, no larger than a leaf, feeding on buds.

Imagine that, blindfolded again, you enter an unfamiliar room. Using your other senses, how much can you learn about this room?

Your ears, listening to sounds, tell you the room is not very large. A breeze tells you a window may be open. You can work your way slowly around the room, touching tables, chairs, and lamps. But even hours of patient exploring would tell you less than your eyes could see at a glance!

Your senses work together.

Once a scientist invited guests to dinner and served them a fine steak. It was the best of meat, broiled to a turn, properly seasoned. In taste and smell, it was perfect —but the guests could not bring themselves to eat it!

He had colored it bright green with a tasteless, odorless coloring substance. Even when he told his guests what he had done, they could not enjoy their meal. The strange color which they saw with their eyes was a more powerful influence than the appetizing taste and smell.

Some evening blindfold yourself before going to dinner, and ask someone to feed you samples of the foods on the table. You will recognize some of them, but you may be surprised! Some familiar foods may not be recognizable!

Vision also works with your sense of balance. A blind man learns to keep his balance, but it is not easy at first.

With your eyes closed, stand on one foot, hooking the other foot behind your knee. If this seems too easy, try it with your head tipped to one side.

Can you keep your balance? Now try it with your eyes open.

Many of the sounds you hear are signals that say, "Look!"

You hear the noise of an automobile and turn your eyes to see it coming.

"Crack!" Was that a .22, a two-bagger, a stick breaking? Your eyes tell you.

Imagine trying to build a campfire without vision! Or trying to cut a piece of wood, drive a nail, or assemble an airplane model.

You could do most of these things without vision. Blind men do. But vision makes it possible to do them more quickly, more easily. Eyes and hands work best together.

How much of your information about the world is gathered with your eyes?

Some people say nine-tenths. But if every detail is considered, this estimate is much too low.

Suppose, when you were blindfolded in an unfamiliar room, someone tried to describe it to you. If he talked for a long time, he could mention every object in the room. But he would miss many little things—a spot on the wallpaper, for example.

A picture might be hanging on the wall of the room. How would he describe it? Try it yourself! Choose a picture in a magazine and try to describe it to someone who has not seen it. Even if you do the job well, it will take several minutes. But his eyes would see the entire picture in a few seconds.

Before television, baseball games were described by radio broadcasters. It was interesting, but not like being at the ball park. Then came TV—but even television is not like being at the game.

Your eyes have far more capacity than a television camera. Sitting in the bleachers, you see thousands of details the camera cannot catch. You can see the pitcher winding up, the batter getting ready, the runners taking their signals from the base-line coaches. And, almost in the same instant, you see the hot-dog salesman catching a quarter tossed to him, the man next to you marking his score card, an airplane flying overhead.

In a TV broadcast, someone else decides what to show on the screen. When you're at the ball game there are thousands of events and details within your range of vision. You choose what to look at. You can make a dozen choices in the time it takes the TV camera to swing from home plate to first.

This is one of the most wonderful and valuable qualities of vision. You look directly at only one small part of the scene before you, and it is foremost in your mind. But your eyes can turn to another part of the scene in an instant.

We use vision to observe the world around us—even to observe things we cannot see!

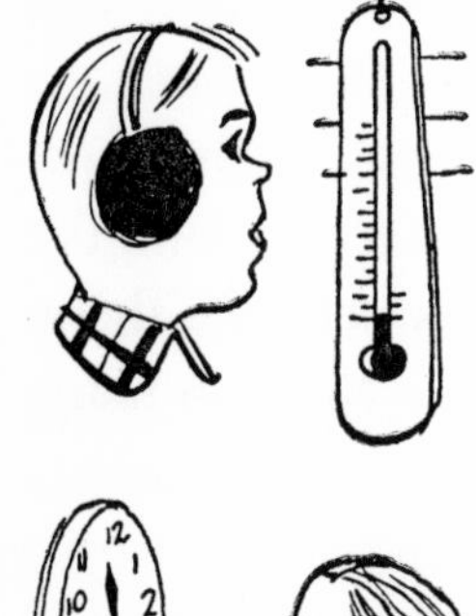

We can feel heat, but our heat sense is not very accurate. To measure temperature, we use a thermometer—which we can see.

We cannot see time passing, though most people can guess the time of day with rough accuracy. But to measure time exactly we use clocks—which we can see.

Electricity is invisible as it flows through wires. It is observed and measured by the use of instruments, which can be read with the eyes.

Some TV shows use applause meters. We can hear applause, but to measure how loud it is we need a device that can be seen.

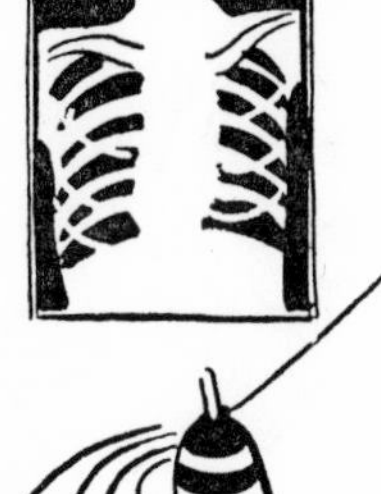

X rays are invisible, but they are used to make a visible image on film. Fishermen often use a bobber, so that they can see when a fish nibbles at their bait.

Vision is swift, and it is tightly linked with the actions of our bodies.

A major-league batter connects with a pitched ball moving at close to 80 miles per hour. A trained boxer moves his head just enough to duck a quick jab.

Seeing—looking at something—doesn't seem difficult. And it isn't. While you can decide to look at something and deliberately turn your eyes to it, most of your eye motions are made without your thinking about them.

But this simple act, looking, makes use of the most intricate and wonderful apparatus known to man: the eye itself, the brain, and the connections between them. No man-made instrument is so sensitive. No man-made machine is so complex.

In the chapters that follow, you will see how your eyes work. You will perform experiments with your eyes and make some discoveries about your own vision.

You will see what vision means to airplane pilots, artists, magicians, and astronomers, why motion pictures seem to move, and how your vision is fooled by optical illusions. You will learn what an "observant" person does —a woodsman or a reporter—and test your own observation.

But let's begin our adventures in seeing.

THE LIGHT WE SEE

SUPPOSE A black blindfold were placed over your eyes. You could not see. The room, the house, all the world would still be there around you, but you would see nothing.

Of course you could still touch objects, feel their shape, their weight, and whether they were warm or cold. You could still taste, smell, and hear. Even blindfolded, you could explore and make discoveries.

Then, while you were still blindfolded, suppose someone were to hand you an object.

What is it?

You touch it with your fingers and weigh it. It's round, but not as perfectly round as a ball. The surface is smooth and waxy. Your fingers find a little stem.

You smell it, then bite into it. It's an apple!

It took you only a few seconds to recognize the object. But even now there are some things you don't know about it—for example, is it red, yellow, or green?

With your eyes, you would have recognized the apple in a split second. And you could have seen it across the room or growing high in an apple tree.

Suppose now, instead of being blindfolded, you were in a totally dark room. It would not be easy to find such a room. There is almost always some light outdoors, and it filters in through window shades and blinds. But imagine one. You sit there, and again someone hands you an object.

Your eyes are open, but you cannot see it.

Light a candle—and you see it.

What does the candlelight do?

Put a dark screen between the lighted candle and the object. You can see the candle, but not the object.

Now put the screen between the candle and your eyes. You can see the object, but not the candle.

To see an apple, eyes and an apple are not enough. There must be light. The light must fall on the apple. It must be reflected from the apple. We see light, reflected from the apple to our eyes.

If you perform the first experiment, you may be able to see the apple even with a screen between the apple and the candle. Why?

Some light is reflected from the walls, the ceiling and other objects. Light travels in all directions, and is reflected in all directions.

This will be true in all the experiments we perform in a darkened room. You can improve the results by shielding the light.

For example, the next experiment makes use of a flashlight. You can make a cardboard tube to slip around the flashlight, so that its light travels only through the tube.

We see reflected light. Some objects reflect more light than others.

Use a table with a dark wood top, or covered with a dark-colored cloth. Place on it several objects: a red apple, white paper, a yellow book, a piece of black velvet.

Darken the room and turn on the flashlight. Shine it on each object.

The white paper is brightest, reflecting the most light. Yellow is next, then red. The black velvet reflects very little light.

True black reflects no light at all. But there are few really black materials. Most "black" objects are dark gray, or they have a surface film or fuzz that reflects some light.

Suppose you were to fasten a piece of red glass or plastic over the flashlight lens, so that it cast a red light. Now the white paper would look reddish, and the yellow book would look reddish, too. The apple would still be red, the black velvet darker than before.

We see reflected light. If only red light is present, only red light can be reflected.

Where does light come from? There are many sources: the sun, the stars, electric lights, fires. Most light sources are hot.

Light and heat are both forms of energy. They travel in waves, very rapidly. The sun is 93,000,000 miles away, but its light and heat reach the earth in only eight minutes.

From their source, heat and light waves travel in all directions, spreading out rapidly. You have seen waves traveling in water, on the surface of a pond. If you toss a rock in the water, circles of waves spread out.

Sound waves travel in air—or through water or solid materials. But energy waves of heat and light will travel through empty space, much faster than sound waves. They will also travel through air, glass, and other transparent materials. You have often felt the sun's warmth through a closed window even when the outside air is cold.

Some waves are longer than others. Here, for example,

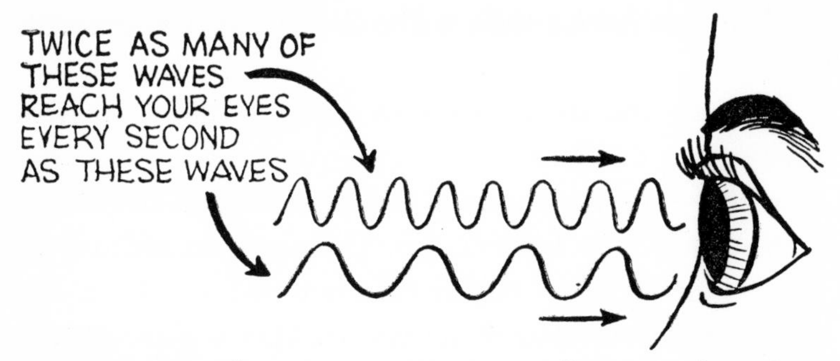

are two sets of waves, one twice as long as the other.

If both sets of waves traveled at the same speed, twice as many of the short waves would reach a certain point—your eye, for example—each second.

There are many kinds of energy waves: heat, light, radio waves, X rays. Their chief difference is in their length. Radio waves are very long, X rays very short. Light waves are those to which the human eye responds.

There is a broad spectrum of such energy waves. Radio waves have lengths ranging from several hundred miles down to less than one one-hundredth of an inch. Heat waves are shorter. Waves of visible light are shorter still, 40,000 to 60,000 of them per inch. Then come very much shorter waves: those of ultraviolet, X rays, and gamma rays. Visible light waves are a tiny part of this vast spectrum.

The wave length of light waves determines the color you see. The longest visible waves, closest to heat waves, are those of red light.

If you switch on an electric toaster and hold your hand near it, you can feel heat while the coils are still dark. As they become hotter they begin to glow, first a dull red, then orange, then yellow.

Heat waves are sometimes called infrared waves, which means "below red" in the spectrum. Your family may have an infrared lamp which gives off heat waves; it also glows, because it gives off some visible light.

The shortest visible waves are violet. Next on the spectrum are ultraviolet waves, "above violet" on the spectrum.

There are special films made which will take photographs by infrared and ultraviolet light, light the human eye cannot see.

The sun's light is white. Later we will see how this white light can be taken apart, spread out into all of the colors of the spectrum of visible light, from red to violet, and how these colors can be mixed to make white light.

A "red" object is one that reflects only red light waves. When white light, such as sunlight, falls on it, the red light waves are reflected, the others absorbed. A "green" object is one that absorbs all but green light waves.

Color is the eye's response to different wave lengths of visible light.

Some lights are brighter than others. The sun is too bright to look at directly. A candle's flame is too dim to light an entire room.

Here are two sets of waves. Both have the same wave length. But one set is bigger than the other:

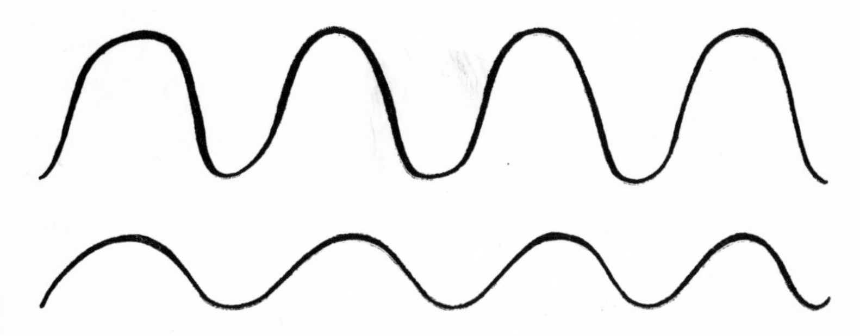

THE BIGGER WAVES ARE WAVES OF BRIGHTER LIGHT

The bigger waves are those of brighter, more intense light. The two lights are the same color, but one is brighter.

Light a candle in a dark room and hold a printed page close to it. Slowly carry the page away from the candle to the opposite end of the room. The light reflected from the page will become dimmer and dimmer, until finally there is too little light for you to read the page.

If you throw a rock into a pond, you see the waves flatten out as they spread across the surface. Light becomes dimmer as it travels from its source, because it spreads out and covers a much larger area. You cannot stand close to a blazing fire, but some distance away you cannot feel the heat waves.

How fast do light waves move?

They travel 186,000 miles in a second, more than seven times the distance around the world!

Sound waves, traveling in air, travel much slower, little more than one mile in five seconds.

You may have seen a carpenter working some distance away. You see his hammer fall, then a little later, hear the sound.

You see the light of a flash of lightning. By counting the seconds before you hear the thunder, you can tell how far away the lightning struck.

What do we see?

We see light. Vision is our response to light, light from a glowing source, such as the sun, or light reflected from the objects around us.

BENDING LIGHT

HAVE YOU ever looked through the little telescope of a surveyor's theodolite or transit? It is like an ordinary telescope, except for tiny cross hairs inside.

What does the surveyor see when he looks through it? He sees light reflected from distant objects. He moves the telescope until the cross hairs cut across the exact center of an object he selects. Then he knows his transit is pointed directly at that object.

Why? Because light travels in straight lines.

In making his survey, the surveyor could stretch a string between the place where he stands and the distant object. But it is quicker and more accurate for him to use straight lines of light.

You can make an experiment to demonstrate that light travels in straight lines. You will need a candle, a sheet of black paper, a sheet of white paper, and a room that can be made dark.

Fasten the white paper on the wall, like a motion-picture screen. Make a hole in the black paper by pushing a pin through it—not the head, just the shank.

Light the candle and hold it a few feet from the screen. Now hold the black paper between them, so the only light falling on the screen passes through the pinhole.

What do you see? An image of the candle flame—upside down!

Why? Take a look at this picture.

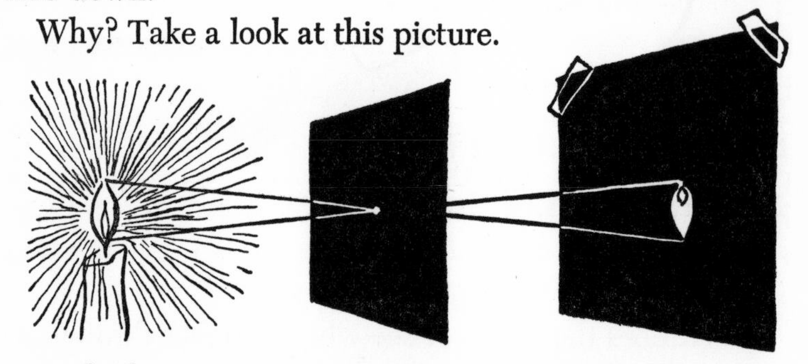

Light from a point at the tip of the candle flame travels in all directions. Only one beam of this light can pass through the pinhole. It travels in a straight line and makes a bright point on the screen.

Light from another point at the base of the flame also travels in all directions. The beam that passes through the pinhole makes another point on the screen, *above* the first point. They crossed each other at the pinhole.

All of the many points of light on the flame combine to build the flame's image, upside down.

The image of the flame is dim. Let's make it brighter.

With the point of a sharp pencil, make the pinhole a little larger. Now more light can get through, but the image of the flame is blurred. Why?

More beams of light from a point at the flame's tip can pass through. Instead of making a tiny point of light on the screen, they make a circle of light.

Each point of light on the flame sends a circle of light to the screen. The circles overlap. The image is brighter, but blurred.

Enlarge the hole still more, until it is as big around as the pencil. Now the spot on the screen is much brighter, but the image of the flame is too blurred to see.

Very little of the candle's light passed through your pinhole. Imagine that the flame was at the center of a hollow ball. The ball measures 1 foot from center to surface. If a pinhole were pricked in the ball's surface, what part of the candle's light could pass through?

Less than one-millionth! So, if you held the black paper a foot from the candle flame, less than a millionth of its light passed through and fell on the screen.

When the hole is made larger, more light passes through. Here are two holes. The larger will admit 100 times as much light.

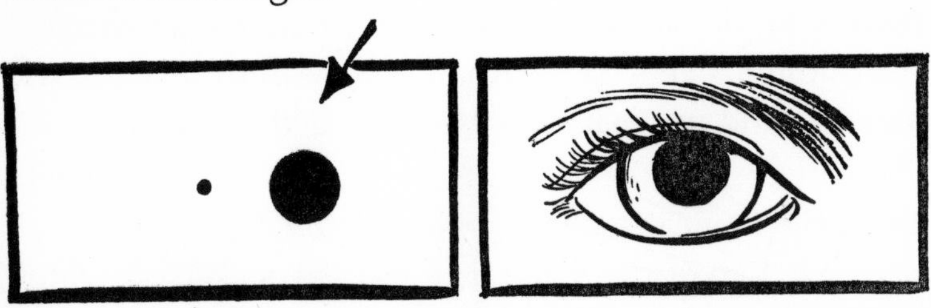

Look at your eye in a mirror. In the center is a black opening, the pupil. Light passes through this hole. Is there some kind of screen inside?

There is. But the pupil is much larger than a pinhole. Why isn't the image on the screen blurred? Is there some way of admitting more light, using a larger hole, and still having a sharp image?

For this experiment you will need a magnifying glass.

Light the candle in a dark room, as you did before. Place it about ten feet from the screen.

Instead of using the black paper with the pinhole, hold the magnifying glass between the candle flame and the screen.

At first you will see only a circle of light. Move the magnifying glass back and forth, nearer to and farther from the screen, until the image is sharp and clear.

Again you have an upside-down image of the flame, but much brighter than before.

Your magnifying glass is a *lens*. This kind of lens gathers the light that falls on it and brings it into *focus*.

How does it do it?

First let's figure out what it must do. Light from a point at the flame's tip, traveling in straight lines in all directions, will fall on the lens.

For the image to be sharp, this light must be gathered together and brought back to a point, like this:

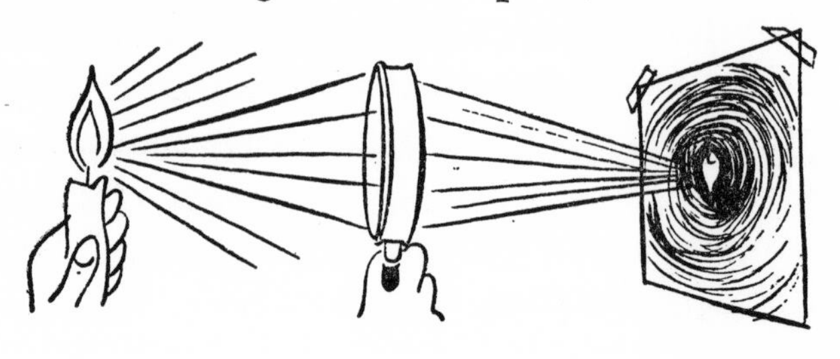

This is exactly what a lens of this kind does. It bends light.

How does it do it?

Light travels at 186,000 miles a second in empty space. It travels a little more slowly in air, more slowly still in water, glass, and other dense but transparent substances.

Light from the candle flame travels through air to the lens. It travels more slowly passing through the lens. When it comes out on the other side, it speeds up again.

Imagine a column of boys in coaster wagons, four abreast. At first they make good speed on hard pavement. Then the column comes to a triangular plot of grass.

The first wagon slows down when it meets the grass. An instant later the second wagon reaches the grass, then the third, then the fourth. By now the front of the column has been turned, in order to keep the front rank lined up.

The fourth wagon has the shortest stretch of grass to cover, so it is the first to reach hard pavement and pick up speed again. By the time the first wagon reaches the pavement, the column front has been turned still farther from its original direction.

This is what happens to a beam of light when it passes through a triangular piece of glass. It is bent when it enters the glass and again when it comes out on the other side.

Let's put two triangles of glass base to base, like this:

Then we round them off, like this:

And there is your magnifying glass!

A magnifying glass is a lens, which bends light. This shape of lens is called *convex*.

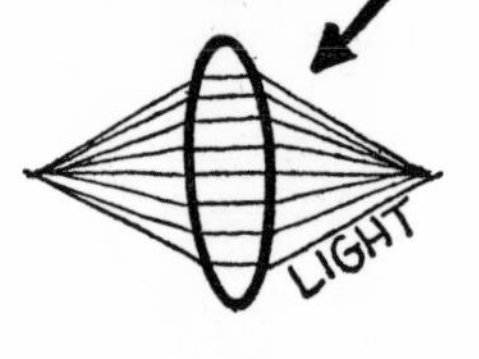

Look at your eye in the mirror, or look at another person's eye. The surface of the eye, in front of the pupil, is shaped like a convex lens. You can see transparent material, like glass, between the surface and the pupil.

Light is bent when it reaches the eye, so that a sharp image is formed on the screen inside the eye.

In the experiment with the magnifying glass, you had to find the right place to hold the glass to make the image sharp. Does the shape of the lens make a difference?

Of course it does, as you can see by looking back at the boys with the coaster wagons. How far they are turned from their original direction depends on the shape of the grassy plot.

A thick lens bends light more than a thin lens:

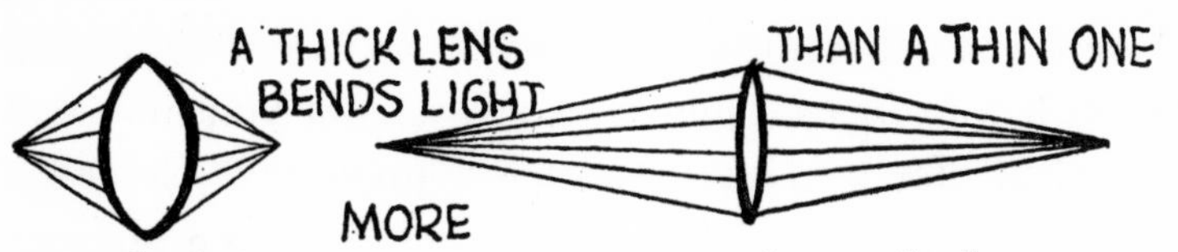

We have more experiments to make with the magnifying glass. Until now we have used a candle flame, because a brighter light would cause too much reflection from the walls and ceiling. But now it will be easier to use a table lamp with a bare light bulb.

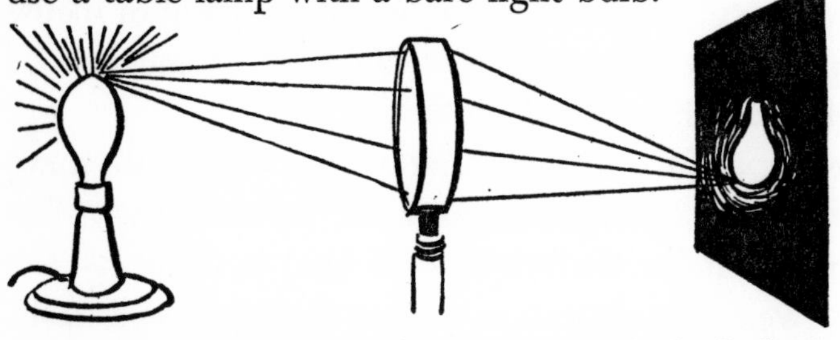

First, let's repeat the experiment with the light, magnifying glass, and screen.

When you have made a sharp image, ask someone to move the lamp a little farther away, while you hold the magnifying glass. Do you have to move the glass again to keep the image clear?

Does the whole surface of a lens gather light?

Punch a pencil-size hole in a piece of paper, and use the paper to cover the lens while you repeat the experiment. The image is clear, but dimmer. Move the paper around on the lens, so that the hole is first near the center, then near the edge.

If you do this carefully, without moving the lens, the image will not move.

Here is further proof that the lens gathers light and brings it into focus. One more experiment you may like best of all, for it seems almost like magic:

Trace the outline of the magnifying glass on a piece of paper. Punch five or six pencil-size holes inside the circle. Cover the lens with this circle.

Now, with the light turned on, hold the glass near the screen. You will see five or six spots of light.

Move the glass slowly away, to find the point of focus. The spots move closer together. Finally they merge into a single sharp image!

The shape of the holes doesn't matter. Try it with some irregular holes torn in the paper.

The more holes, the brighter the final image.

Now we are ready to have a look inside the eye itself. We know now that we see light, usually reflected light. We know that the light passes through the dark hole of the pupil and that it is gathered by a lens to bring it into focus inside.

We know something else: the image on the screen inside the eye must be upside down!

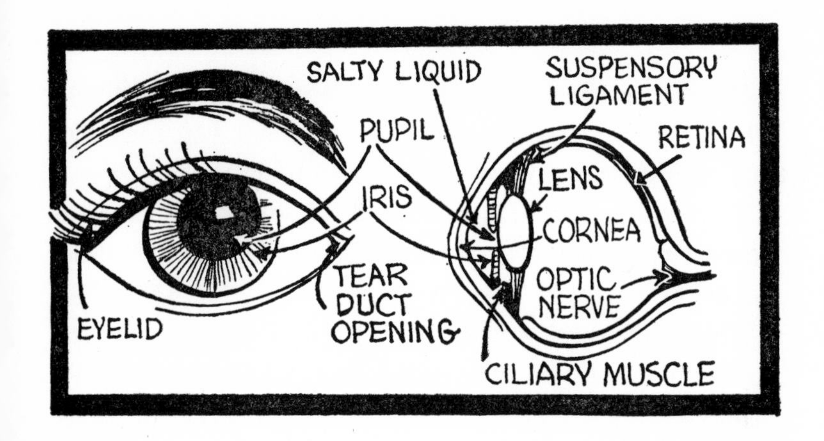

INSIDE YOUR EYE

LOOK CLOSELY at your eyes in a mirror. What can you see? You have two eyes, of course, just about the same in appearance, moving together as you look from point to point.

You can see the eyelids, which blink to keep the eyeball moist and wash away dust. They blink as often as twenty times a minute, and they blink shut to protect the eyes when some object flies toward them.

You can see the eyelashes and, beyond the roots of the eyelashes, the tiny openings from which a special lubricant is supplied. Near the nose you can see the opening of the tear duct, through which tears sometimes flow into the nose.

The eye itself, the part you can see, looks somewhat like part of a ball—and this is quite correct. The eye is shaped like a ball, only part of which is exposed.

The *pupil* is an opening in the eyeball through which

light passes. It is surrounded by the doughnut-shaped ring, the *iris.*

The eyeball is enclosed by a tough membrane. There is a transparent window set into this membrane, where it covers the iris and pupil. This window is the *cornea.*

The space between the cornea and pupil is filled with a clear, salty liquid.

Now we come to parts of the eye you cannot see. You could catch a glimpse of them through the instruments used by doctors.

Behind the pupil is the *lens.*

It is really an extra lens, for the cornea and the liquid it encloses also bend light. The lens is surrounded by the *ciliary muscle,* which can change the shape of the lens by contracting.

The eyeball is filled with a gelatinlike material, a clear substance.

The screen on which the image is projected is at the back of the eyeball. It is called the *retina.*

The retina is a mass of special cells, sensitive to light. These cells are connected to nerve fibers which are gathered together in the *optic nerve,* leading to the brain.

The eyeball is held by a series of muscles which can turn it up and down and from side to side.

These are the principal parts of the eye. What happens when light, reflected from some object, reaches the eye?

If the pupil were as tiny as a pinhole, some part of the light would pass through. No lens would be needed, but the image would be dim.

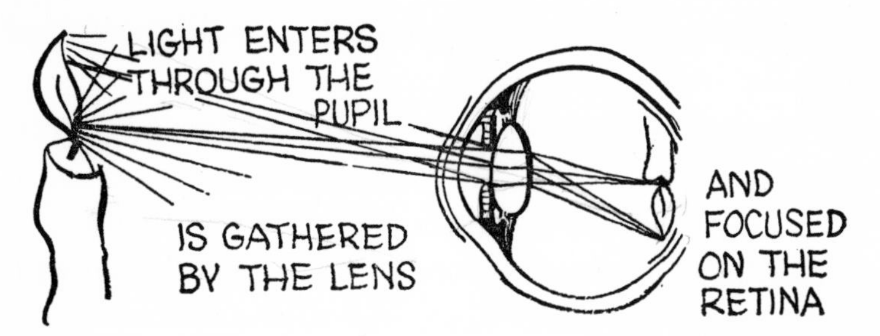

Because of the eye's lenses, the pupil can be larger than a pinhole, admitting more light. The light is gathered by the lens and focused on the retina.

But wait! When you experimented with the magnifying glass, you found that you had to move it forward or back when the light was moved forward or back. If you focused an image with the light 6 feet from the screen, it would be blurred when the light was moved to 12 feet away.

In the same way, if the lens of the eye is shaped to focus a sharp image 6 feet away, how can you also see a more distant object clearly?

Does something change? Let's see:

The best way to perform this experiment is by looking through an ordinary window screen.

First look at the screen, so that you see it sharply. Move as close to the screen as you can and still hold a sharp image of it. It may help to close one eye.

Now look *through* the screen at an object outside. The instant you do so, the sharp image of the screen is gone. It is blurred, out of focus!

Something in the eye changed. And, with another experiment, you can *feel* it change.

Close one eye and hold up a finger, 2 feet from the open eye.

Look at it. Keep it in focus.

Keeping it in focus, move it slowly toward your eye. Keep every line of your fingerprint ridges in sharp focus.

How close can you move the finger and keep it in focus? Try harder!

Did you feel that strain, the feeling of relaxation when you looked away again?

What you felt was the ciliary muscle contracting, trying to squeeze the lens of the eye—make it thicker—to focus a sharp image. You made it squeeze as hard as it could.

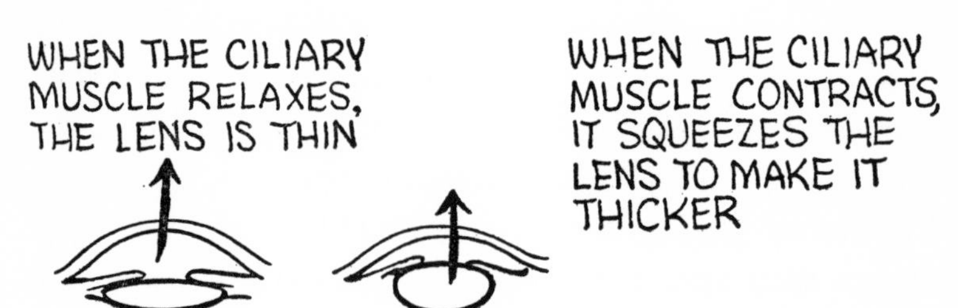

Usually, the process happens so easily that you don't notice it. You just *look* and your eye is focused.

But sometimes you may be nodding or daydreaming over a book and the printed letters become blurred. Your ciliary muscles are relaxing, too.

This focusing mechanism is very quick and accurate. But some people have difficulty in focusing.

For example, one person may have eyes that measure a little less than normal from front to back. The lens is too close to the retina. To make the image sharp, the ciliary muscle would have to make the lens thicker than normal, when this person looked at a near object.

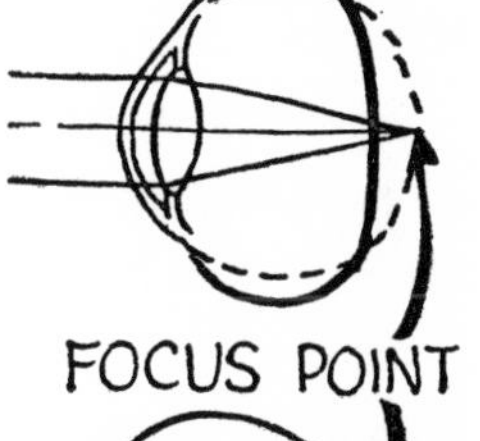

Can it be done? Not always. There is a limit to such thickening. You discovered this fact when you tried to focus on your finger close to your eye. Even with normal eyes you cannot focus on an object an inch or two away.

The person whose eyes are shorter than normal cannot see nearby objects clearly. He is "farsighted." The distant horizon may be sharp, but he may be unable to focus a sharp image of an object across the room.

Another person may be nearsighted. His eyes are longer than normal from front to back. He can see near objects clearly. But even when his ciliary muscles are fully relaxed, the lens does not become thin enough to bring distant objects into sharp focus.

These are simple problems of light bending. The remedy is eyeglasses, equipped with proper lenses.

These lenses help the eye to bend light. With their aid farsighted and nearsighted persons can focus on near or far objects.

As a person becomes older, the lens of the eye loses some of its elasticity. The ciliary muscle cannot thicken it quite so much. He may need glasses for reading, therefore, even if he did not need them before.

If the difficulty is more severe, he may need two pairs of eyeglasses, with different lenses: one pair for reading, another for seeing more distant objects.

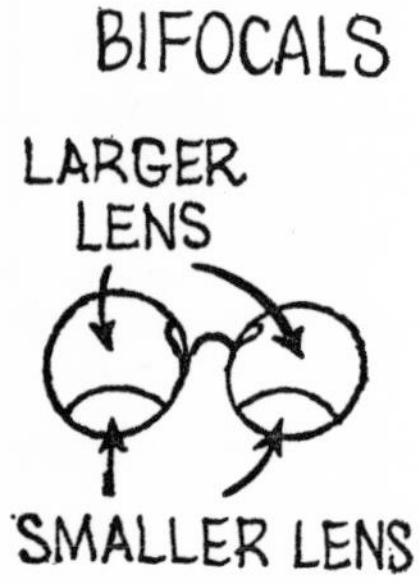

"Bifocals" are eyeglasses with two sets of lenses. For general vision the wearer looks through the larger lens. For reading he looks through the smaller.

Some people, especially actors and athletes, wear "contact lenses." These are tiny transparent shells which are placed right on the eye. Some of them cover only the cornea. They are almost invisible—which is important for actors—and they are less dangerous than spectacles if one plays football.

These shells are curved, and the space between the shell and cornea is filled with tears or a liquid like tears. Thus they become a part of the eye's lens, changing its shape so light is correctly bent.

More people wear eyeglasses than contact lenses, partly because the average person can wear contact lenses for only a few hours at a time—so he needs eyeglasses, too. But there are some conditions, such as a misshapen cornea, which only contact lenses can correct.

The lens of the eye is not its only adjustable part.

Look at your pupils in a mirror under a bright light. Then look at them in a dim light, just enough light to see by.

See how much larger they become?

In dim light, the pupils open to admit more light. This adjustment helps us to see well under differing conditions. When the sun is very bright and dazzling, the pupils contract as much as they can, reducing the amount of light that strikes the retina. But, if they could not open as wide as they do, we should be almost blind at twilight.

Now you know the first steps in seeing.

Light is reflected from objects.

The light travels to the eyes. It passes through the lenses of the eyes, where it is bent, so that an image is focused on the retina.

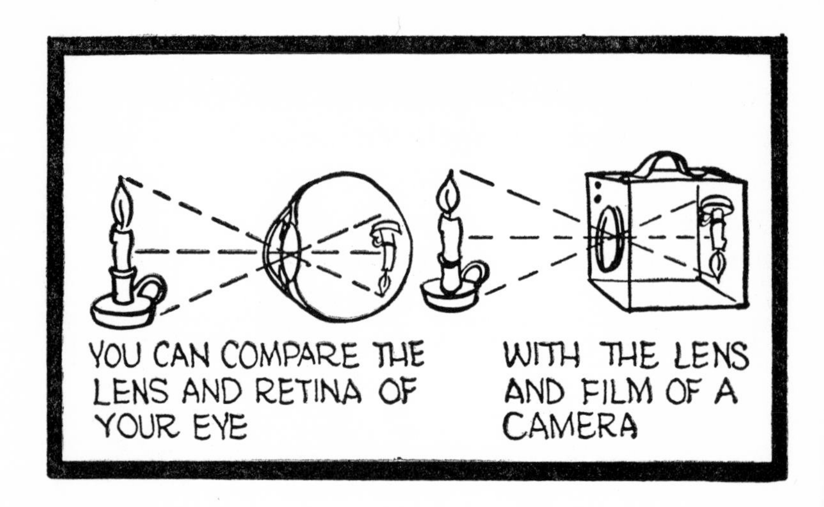

THE SCREEN OF THE EYE

THE IMAGE focused by the lens of the eye falls on the "screen" at the back of the eyeball, the *retina.*

The retina is a kind of carpet, made up of tiny light-sensitive cells.

How tiny are they? It's hard to believe, but each retina has about 130,000,000 cells.

There are 60,000 dots in the rectangle below.

To print 130,000,000 dots of this size would require a

sheet of paper 10 feet long and 9 feet wide. Yet this number of cells is packed together in the small space at the back of the eye.

There are two types of cells in the retina. They are called "rods" and "cones," because they look something like rods and cones under a microscope.

Both types of cells are sensitive to light, but each has a different use.

The rods are used for general perception of light. They are more sensitive to dim light than the cone cells. Rods provide night vision.

The cones are used to see color and fine detail. You are reading these words with your cone cells.

Birds that fly mostly at night have retinas made up almost entirely of rod cells. Hawks have keen vision by day because their retinas contain mostly cone cells.

What do you see at night?

If the moon is not bright and there are no artificial lights near, you see gray, fuzzy outlines. You see light and shadow, but not color. You could see the page of an open book, but you could not read the printed words. The old saying is true: "At night all cats are gray."

With a little more light, perhaps from a flashlight, the cone cells are stimulated. You can see color and fine detail.

There are twenty times as many rods as there are cones. Over most of the retina, rods are much more numerous.

But at the center, directly behind the pupil, there are no rods whatever.

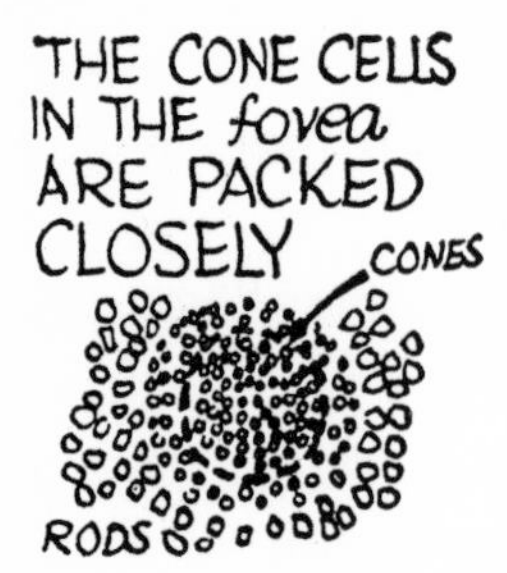

At the center is a small pit, called the *fovea centralis,* surrounded by a yellowish patch, the *macula.* In and around the *fovea centralis* is a mass of cone cells, packed closely together. Within this small area your vision is sharpest.

You can see this entire page at once. But when you read, only two or three words can be read at one time. Beyond a small circle at the very center of your vision, you cannot see the fine detail of printed letters.

Let's make some experiments to demonstrate this:

Hold two match folders side by side at normal reading distance. It may seem that you can read all the words on both folders without moving your eyes. But if you concentrate, you'll find this isn't so.

Choose a point on one of the folders and look directly at it. Without looking away, can you read anything on the other folder?

Still looking at a point on one folder, move the other a few inches to the side. You can still see it. But words are not recognizable. Let's try to find out how large this "reading area" is.

Cut a circle of paper about the size of a half dollar. Make a cross at the center. Then place the circle over a printed paragraph.

Look directly at the cross. Can you recognize words beyond the circle?

Make the circle smaller, the size of a quarter. Try it with a circle as small as a dime.

You may find it easier to make this experiment with one eye closed.

Even though the area of sharp focus is very small, you can learn to read with a larger section of the retina. When you read frequently, you become familiar with the general shape and appearance of words. You recognize them at a glance, even if they are fuzzy or incomplete.

For example:

You can read these words

What do your eyes do when you read?

Watch someone reading. It's better to do so when he does not know you are watching.

If you look closely, you will see that he moves his eyes in quick little jumps. In reading a book, his eyes make

several jumps in scanning each line, then a longer jump back to the beginning of the next line.

Can you count the number of jumps his eyes make in reading each line?

The sharp-focus area is only large enough for a word of about eight letters of this size, or a combination of short words such as "of the" or "in his." The average book has about ten words or short combinations in each line of type.

If a reader looks at each word, bringing it into sharp focus, his eyes must make ten jumps to read one line.

A rapid reader does not look at every word. Instead of ten jumps, his eyes make only three to five jumps for each line.

While his eyes are looking directly at one word, he can see—though not clearly—the general shape and appearance of the next few words. If they seem familiar, his eyes skip over them on the next jump.

Do you do this, too? Here is a test that will tell you:

Cover a printed page with a sheet of paper. Move the sheet of paper slowly to the right, so that the left side of the sheet uncovers the words one at a time.

See how fast you can read this way.

Now try it using the sheet of paper to cover up the words as fast as you read them.

You will probably find that the first method makes your reading much slower, the second makes no difference. The first method makes it impossible for your eye to see what's coming next.

You see fine detail only within that little patch of concentrated cone cells. But your whole field of vision is very wide, perhaps very much wider than you realize.

Before we experiment, make a guess!

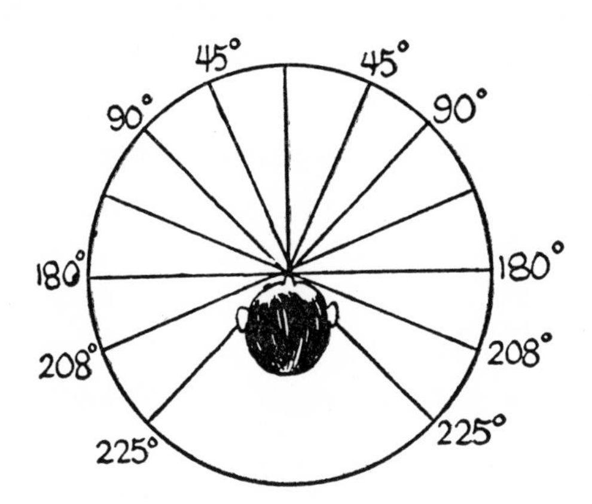

Here is a picture of your head. A circle is drawn around it.

With a pencil, fill in—very lightly—the area you think you can see with your eyes pointing straight ahead.

How many degrees did you guess?

Now let's experiment to find out how much you can really see.

You'll need a helper. Have him stand behind you. He should hold in his hand, at eye level, some object—such as a match folder—without telling you what it is.

Look straight ahead, being careful not to move your eyes. Have him move his hand slowly from behind, into your field of vision, without telling you whether it is approaching from the left or right. As soon as you detect any motion, say "Stop!"

Repeat this several times, on each side. Whenever you say "Stop!" your helper should drop the object to the floor, marking the place where it lands.

If you stretch a string from the place where the object lands to the base of your big toe, you will have the angle of vision with which to compare your guess.

This kind of seeing is called *peripheral vision*. The average person has about 208 degrees of peripheral vision.

Each eye has more than half of 208 degrees, because the two fields of vision overlap.

Did you notice something in making that experiment? If your helper jiggled the object and kept it moving, you could see it sooner than if he moved it slowly and quietly.

Try it again to demonstrate that.

How good is peripheral vision?

Repeat the experiment as before. But this time don't have your helper stop as soon as you detect motion. Have him continue moving the object forward until you can recognize and describe it.

To perform this experiment successfully takes real concentration on your part. Your eyes have been trained to turn, quickly, to look at a moving object. You may not be able to continue looking straight ahead.

A second helper may be necessary. Have him stand in front of you. You look into his eyes, and have him look into yours. If you look away, even for an instant, he can tell.

You can make an interesting game of experiments with peripheral vision.

You can see an object off to one side. But what do you see? Can you recognize its shape? Can you see color?

Can you tell whether it is moving toward you or away from you?

Peripheral vision is very useful, even though it may seem to be limited.

Make two tubes. The cores of toilet-paper rolls are about the right size. Or cut both ends out of two small frozen-orange-juice cans.

Hold these tubes to your eyes.

Now try walking around the room.

Looking through the tubes, most of your peripheral vision is cut off. You see clearly—but only straight ahead.

With such limited vision you would be poor at most sports.

In football an end breaks loose and goes streaking down the field. A forward pass shoots from behind the scrimmage line.

The end doesn't look at the passer. He sees the flying ball with his peripheral vision. Only at the last moment does he look directly at the ball. And when he does, his peripheral vision sees the tackler closing in; he twists to avoid him without ever looking right at him.

Automobile drivers use peripheral vision to avoid accidents. While they look at the road ahead, they can also see other cars coming from behind to pass or approaching from side streets.

Sometimes, when you reach for something on a high shelf, you accidentally knock a cup or glass off the shelf. If your hand is quick enough, you may catch the falling object without looking directly at it.

A magician uses your peripheral vision to fool you. He calls it "misdirection."

He knows that your eyes will turn to look at a moving object. So he waves his wand high in the air, in his left hand.

As you look at the wand, his right hand quietly picks up or conceals an object. He must do this gently, with a natural motion, so that your attention is not attracted to this hand. But if he does it skillfully, he can deceive you. You don't see what his right hand is doing, even though you think you are looking right at him.

Have you ever seen a ghost?

Many people think they have. And often they have seen something—something elusive. At night they see something moving, off to one side. But when they look at it, it has vanished. When they look away, it appears in their peripheral vision again.

Can you explain it?

Suppose you were walking at night and a handkerchief was fluttering on a clothesline. If its image fell on the rod cells, cells more sensitive to light than the cones, you might see it in your peripheral vision.

Then, seeing the motion, you would turn your eyes to look right at it. But then the image would fall on the less sensitive cone cells, and you might be unable to see it at all!

Now we know something about the "screen" inside the eye, the retina.

It is made up of 130,000,000 light-sensitive cells, rods and cones.

The image you see is wide and high, but you can see fine detail only in the very center.

You see fine detail and colors with the cone cells, which are packed most tightly together at the center of the retina.

Rods are much more numerous. They respond to very little light. In very dim light you see only with the rod cells, and then you cannot see fine detail or distinguish colors.

SENDING MESSAGES TO THE BRAIN

WHEN LIGHT falls on the rod and cone cells of the retina, what happens?

Suppose you were a scientist trying to find out. Imagine how delicate and difficult your experiments would have to be! Imagine trying to discover what happens inside just one of the 130,000,000 tiny cells of the retina!

An eye can be dissected and studied under a powerful microscope. This will show how the eye is made, but one could only guess how it works. When it is dissected, the eye is not alive, not seeing. It is like studying a television set with the electricity turned off.

Scientists have not solved all the mysteries of the eye, but they have, by many ingenious experiments, discovered most of its principal functions.

They know that when light falls on a light-sensitive cell, a chemical change takes place.

Many living things have cells that sense light.

Some flowers open their petals to the sun and close them at dusk. The sunflower turns to follow the sun across the sky. These flowers do not have eyes, muscles, or brains. Sunlight causes a chemical change in some of the living cells.

An earthworm has no eyes. But he has light-sensitive cells scattered over the surface of his body. He cannot see, but he can sense when part of his body is exposed to the sun.

Most animals have all of their light-sensitive cells grouped in one place, the eye. There are many kinds of animal eyes, but all have retinas, patches of light-sensitive cells.

How can light cause a chemical change?

Have you ever developed a photograph? A camera is somewhat like an eye. It has a lens, which focuses an image. It has a shutter, like the eyelids. It has a diaphragm, like the pupil of the eye. And, in place of the retina, it has a piece of light-sensitive film.

When you take a picture, you click the shutter, allowing light to fall on the film for a fraction of a second. In the darkroom you wash the film in developer. The areas which were exposed to bright light turn dark. Those exposed to very little light, the shadowy parts of the image, remain clear. The light caused a chemical change in the film.

The chemical change in the cells of the eye is much quicker. And it is a *continuous* change. The eye doesn't take a single picture. Each cell responds to the amount of light falling on it each second. The chemicals are constantly being replenished.

Can you think of one problem that makes it difficult for scientists to study this chemical reaction?

Suppose the chemicals in the cells were extracted and put on a glass slide for study. How would a scientist study them? He would have to do much of his work in the dark, because the chemicals change when exposed to light!

This is one reason why the chemical reactions of the cells are still puzzling in some ways. But discoveries have been made. For example, we know that the rod cells, which are most sensitive to light, contain a substance called *visual purple* or *rhodopsin.*

The ancient Egyptians knew of a disease called "night blindness." A person with night blindness could see well in bright light, but in dim light he would be totally blind.

Then it was discovered that the disease could often be cured by eating liver. Only after World War I did doctors learn that the ingredient of liver which cured the disease was Vitamin A.

Vitamin A is also supplied by eating carrots and green leafy vegetables.

In World War II, a rumor began circulating—perhaps started deliberately to fool the Nazis—that our night flyers were improving their night vision by eating lots of carrots. It wasn't true, because Vitamin A won't make normal night vision better. It will cure night blindness in people who have had poor diets. But the average diet supplies plenty of Vitamin A, and night blindness is almost unknown in the United States.

What does Vitamin A do?

The chemical in the rod cells, rhodopsin, is purple in color—in the dark. When light falls on it, it bleaches, first turning yellow, then colorless. Scientists have found that this colorless substance is a mixture of a protein called *opsin* with Vitamin A. In the dark, opsin and Vitamin A combine to restore the supply of rhodopsin, visual purple. When rhodopsin is exposed to light, it bleaches.

So on bright days, there is very little rhodopsin in the rod cells. But in the dark, the supply increases, making the rod cells more sensitive to any small amount of light present.

Suppose you go to the movies on a bright, sunny afternoon. When you first enter the theater, you can hardly see. If you try to find a seat, you may sit down in someone's lap.

After a few minutes your vision improves and you can see better. Before long you can look around and recognize friends in the audience.

Many people think that "getting used to the dark" means their pupils open wider. The pupils do, but this takes only a second or two.

The supply of visual purple builds up more slowly. In five minutes there is enough to improve your vision in the dark, so that you can find your seat. But it continues to build up for as long as half an hour.

Your rod cells are adjustable. By changing the supply of visual purple, they respond to bright or dim light. Your cone cells have this adjustment also, but it is much smaller in extent, and it is all over within five minutes.

How does the chemical change send a message to the brain?

Have you ever seen a photoelectric cell? When light falls on such a cell, it generates a tiny electric current.

Here is a photographer's light meter. When light falls on the photoelectric cell, it generates a tiny electric current, which causes the pointer to swing across the dial.

Some stores have automatic doors controlled by photoelectric cells. A beam of light falls on the cell. When your body breaks the beam, the flow of electricity is cut off. This is a signal to the machinery that opens the door.

A photoelectric cell sends an electrical message. The chemical change in a rod or cone cell of the eye touches off a nerve impulse which travels to the brain.

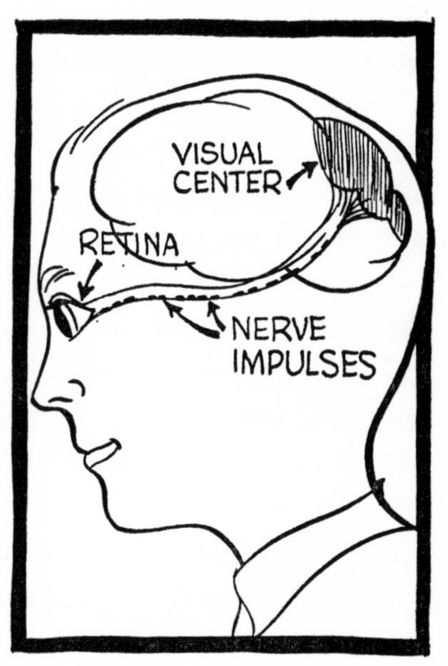

A nerve impulse is something like an electrical current, but not quite the same. Unlike electric wires, nerves are alive. A dead nerve will conduct electricity, but it will not carry a nerve impulse.

A nerve impulse is a change in the living nerve, a

change that travels through it. The chemical reaction in the eye cell starts the impulse, in the section of the nerve fiber attached to the cell. This section passes the impulse to the next, and so on.

You can think of it as a flame traveling along a powder fuse. Each grain of powder that catches fire sets fire to the next grain.

Or you can compare it to an impulse traveling along a stretched spring. If you pluck a spring at one end, the wave travels to the other.

There is an interesting fact about nerve impulses—not just the impulses from the eye, but all impulses in the human nervous system. It is called the "all-or-nothing principle."

Suppose you have a telegraph key connected to a sounder. When you press the key, the sounder clicks.

You can press the key softly or you can hammer on it with all your strength. Whichever you do, the sounder clicks in the same way. You cannot make it click louder or softer. However you press the key, the same message travels to the sounder.

All nerve impulses within a nerve fiber have the same strength! There are no strong or weak impulses.

How, then, do the cells of the retina tell the brain that one light is dim, another bright?

They send *more* impulses when the light is bright. You can't make the telegraph sounder click louder, but you can make it click more often.

Bright light increases the rate of chemical change in

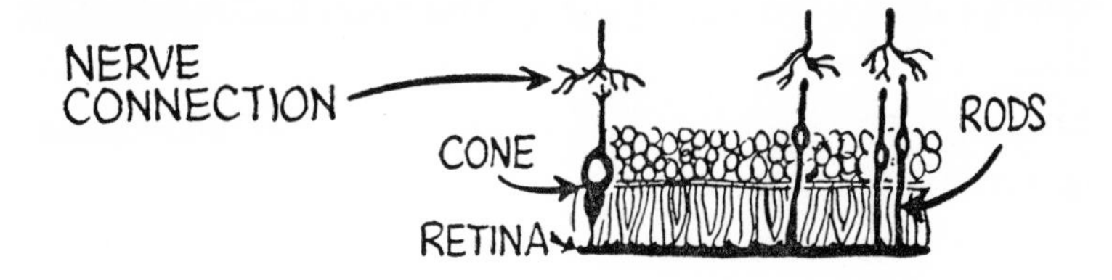

the rod and cone cells. This sets off a more rapid sequence of nerve impulses traveling to the brain.

Each rod and cone cell is connected to a nerve fiber. But this fiber is not a direct path to the brain. Behind the retina there is a network of cross-connections.

Why is night vision, with the rod cells, fuzzy? You know that it is if you have ever tried to read in a very dim light. The rod cells are very sensitive to light. Why is the image you see blurred?

Several rod cells, located near one another, are connected to the same nerve fiber. This increases the sensitivity to light, for instead of carrying the impulses from a single cell, the nerve will carry the combined impulses from several. But this blurs the image, because the brain cannot tell which of the several cells is signaling.

The effect is the same as that of seeing an image out of focus, when light from a single point is not bent back to a single point but falls on a number of cells.

Light-sensitive cells cover the entire retina, except at one spot. This is the place where the nerve fibers are gathered together, where the optic nerve leaves the eye.

You can see this place. Or rather, you can *not* see it. It is a blind spot.

Close your left eye. Look at the cross with your right eye.

Move the page slowly back and forth, nearer to and farther from your eye.

\+ ●

If you keep your eye fixed on the cross, you will find a place where the circle disappears. This is the place where there are no light-sensitive cells. The image falls on that blind spot, and there are no cells to report it to the brain.

Here is another experiment in which you can see a little of the inside of your eye.

Punch a small hole in a card. Now, if the weather is good, go outdoors and look through the hole at a patch of clear sky; look with one eye, closing the other. Hold the card very close to your eye.

Jiggle the card rapidly. Keep it moving quickly, but with very short motions, so that you never stop looking through the hole.

Most people, when they do this, will see a fine network of lines with an opening at the center. The lines are the shadows of the blood vessels which crisscross the retina. The opening is the *fovea,* the area of sharpest vision, where there are no blood vessels.

Now we have another step in the process of vision.

Light is reflected from an object.

It passes through the cornea, pupil, and lens, and an image is focused on the retina.

The light causes a chemical change in the cells.

The chemical change causes nerve impulses to travel to the brain.

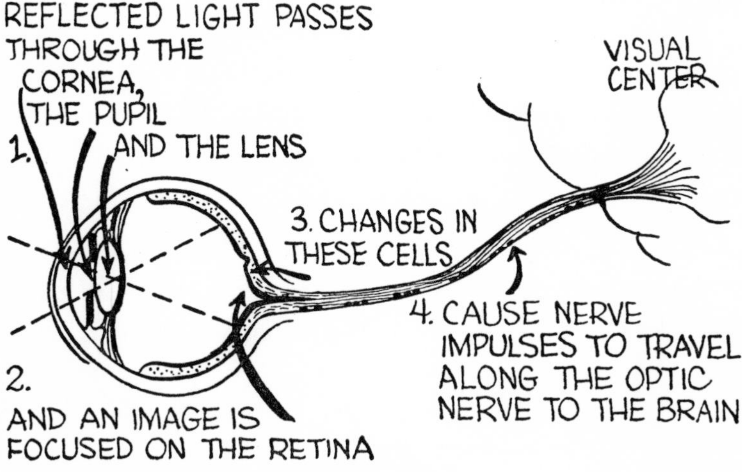

The seeing center of the brain receives millions upon millions of these messages every minute. How does it build up a mental picture?

These nerve fibers lead to the seeing center, at the back of the head. There they are projected upon a "screen." It isn't a screen that reflects light. It is more like a telephone switchboard, where the electric wires that have been twisted in cables are sorted out and arranged in a pattern. Or like one of the big electric display signs in Times Square, New York, where pictures are "drawn" in combinations of thousands of small light bulbs.

You can see how a pattern of impulses can be combined into an image. Here is a picture made up of dots:

Imagine that each dot is a brain cell receiving messages. The heavy dots are cells connected with light-sensitive cells receiving very little light. The tiny dots are messages from cells "seeing" bright light.

There are only about 17,000 dots in this picture.

If you look at it from a distance, the dots disappear, and you see it as a smooth image of gray tones.

You can see how a screen of millions of cells provides a picture with much finer detail.

THE RAINBOW OF COLOR

WHAT A dull world this would be without color! We use the word "colorless" to mean something that is drab, uninteresting.

What if our eyes contained only rod cells, which respond to light but do not distinguish colors? Then we would see only shades of gray. The brilliant plumage of a cardinal would be as dull as that of a cowbird. The blue ocean, the green forest, the rich colors of fabrics and flowers—all would be seen as darker or lighter gray.

What is color?

Color is a sensation, a response of your eye and brain to light.

Visible light is made up of energy waves. They are not all of the same wave length.

The light that causes you to "see red" is made up of the longest visible waves. The shortest visible waves cause you to see the color violet. You see white when the eye receives a mixture of all of the visible wave lengths.

The sun's light is white. When this light falls on an object, a part of the light is absorbed, a part reflected. If all but the longest waves are absorbed, the object looks red. If no visible light was reflected, it would look black.

You can make an experiment with heat waves, which are a little longer than light waves, to see how they are absorbed and reflected.

Take two pieces of ice. Cover one with a black cloth, one with a white cloth, and place them side by side in sunlight.

The ice covered with black cloth will melt more rapidly. The heat waves are absorbed by the black cloth. The white cloth reflects heat waves as it does light waves.

If you ever go camping on a cold night, you can warm your tent by reflection. Build a campfire a safe distance from the tent door. On the opposite side of the fire, place a sheet of polished metal, or hang aluminum foil over a framework of sticks. The shiny surface will reflect heat into the tent.

White light contains all the visible colors. This can be demonstrated by taking white light apart—and by putting it together again.

For thousands of years men saw rainbows in the sky, not knowing why they appeared. Perhaps some noticed that rainbows were seen only when there were drops of water in the air.

They saw rainbows in the spray of waterfalls. On a sunny day you can make a rainbow with the fine spray of a garden hose.

Men must also have seen little rainbows shining near bits of broken glass. Then someone, we do not know who, discovered how to make a rainbow.

In a dark room he arranged for a thin beam of sunlight to enter. In the path of light he placed a triangular glass prism. Beyond the prism was a white screen.

The white sunlight passed through the prism and spread out, forming a rainbow on the screen.

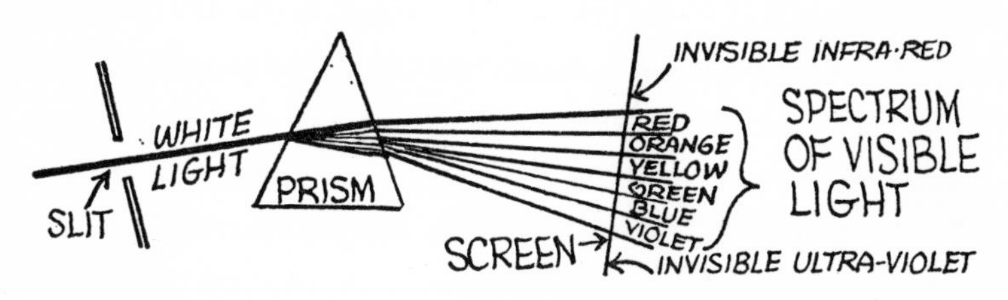

Sir Isaac Newton was the first man to put white light together. He repeated this experiment, but he added a second prism, upside down. The first prism separated white light into its various colors. The second put them together. Only a spot of white light showed on the screen.

What happens to white light when it passes through a prism? As you saw in Chapter 3, the light is bent. The short waves are bent most. Long waves are bent least.

This rainbow is called a spectrum. The colors are always in the same order. Red is always nearest the original direction of the light beam. Violet is always farthest from the original direction.

But, you may ask, why did we not make a rainbow when we bent light by using lenses?

Some cheap lenses do make little rainbows. If you look at a brightly lighted white object through a pair of cheap opera glasses or field glasses, you will see a tiny band of color around the edge of the object.

Good lenses are *color-corrected.* Lens makers have learned how to make lenses combining two kinds of glass so that the light waves come into focus at the same point.

The rainbow does not exhibit all the colors you see around you. But every visible color can be made by combining the colors of the spectrum. In fact, almost all the colors you see are mixtures.

All visible colors can be made by combinations of just three colors of the spectrum: red, blue, and green. These are called the *primary* colors.

What makes an object red, pink, orange or green?

When white light falls on the object, it absorbs some of the colors in white light and reflects others.

If an object were true primary red, it would reflect only the red light.

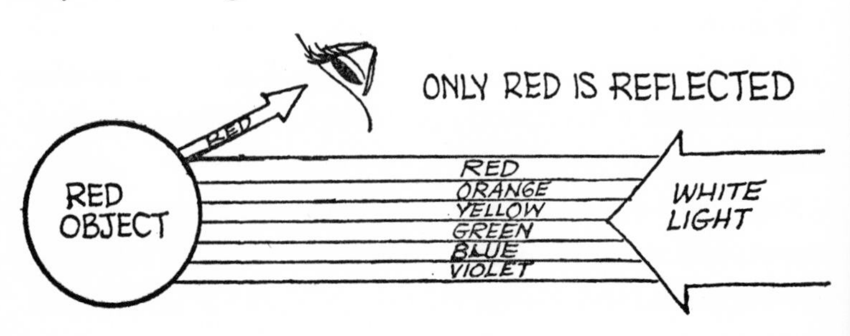

What if a blue or green light fell on a red object? There are no red light waves in blue or green light. No light would be reflected. The object would look black.

But in nature there are almost no objects which are pure red, blue, or green. A tomato, for example, reflects more red waves than waves of other colors. But it does reflect a little blue and green.

Suppose we were to place a number of objects in a row: a white sheet, a red apple, a tomato, a lemon, a plum, and a green leaf. On all of them we shine a beam of primary red light.

What would we see?

All of the objects would look red. But some would be brighter than others.

The white paper, the apple, and the tomato would be brightest. The lemon would be darker, the plum darker still. The green leaf would be almost black, for it reflects very little red. (If it were a true primary green, it would reflect none.)

You have probably heard that white is a mixture of all colors, and perhaps you have tried to make white by mixing the colors in your paintbox.

It didn't work, did it?

Can you figure out, now, why it didn't? Remember that a surface reflects some of the light that falls on it, absorbs the rest.

Suppose you had red paint, which reflects only red waves, and mixed it with blue paint, which absorbs all but blue. The red would absorb everything but red, including the blue. The blue would absorb all but blue, including the red. Only a little red and blue would be reflected. If you added green to the mixture, a little green would be added. But because most of the waves would be absorbed, the reflected light would be gray, not white.

There are experiments which show how mixtures of color are made by *absorption* and *reflection*. We can call them mixtures by *subtraction* (absorption) and *addition*.

It would be fine if you could make these experiments at home. But, unfortunately, it would be almost impossible for you to find materials which are true colors. A piece of glass that looks red to your eye may also reflect some blue and green. And that would make the results confusing.

But here are the experiments, as they have been made in scientific laboratories:

When Newton combined the spectrum, he made white light. We can do the same thing, adding the three primary colors.

We begin with three beams of white light. In the path of each beam we place a color filter, a piece of colored glass. The filters are red, green, and blue. The red filter absorbs all but the red waves; the green all but the green waves; the blue all but the blue waves.

On the screen we see three circles of color: red, green, and blue.

Now we move the projectors so that the circles overlap. The white screen reflects the light that falls on it.

Where they overlap, the screen reflects *mixtures* of colors.

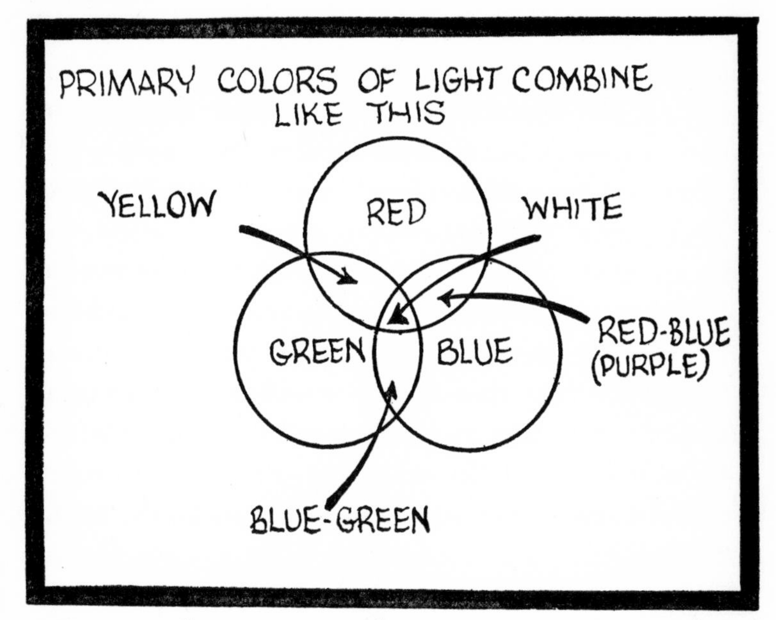

Here is what we see. Where two primaries combine, they make a *complementary* color. Where all three combine, the total is white light.

You may be surprised to see that green is a primary color, and that yellow is a mixture of red and green. You may have mixed yellow and blue paints to make green. Remember that when you mix paints, you *subtract* colors. Yellow paint reflects red and green waves, absorbs blue. The blue paint you used actually contained some green; it absorbed the red waves. Combined, they reflected only the green waves.

Now for experiments with subtraction. We begin with white light, shown here divided into its three primary colors: red, green, and blue. We will use glass filters, colored to subtract some of the white light.

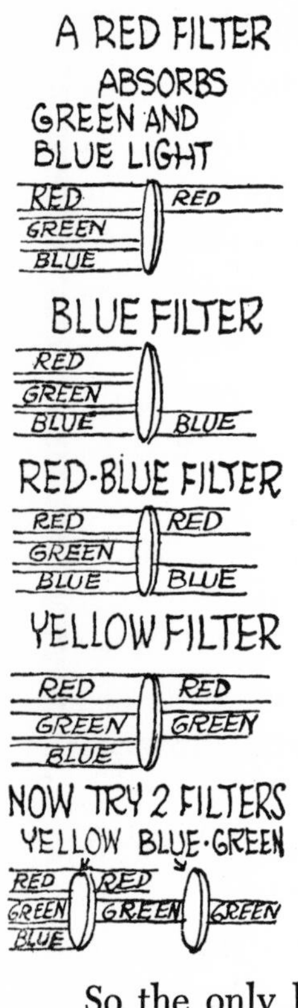

When we use a red filter, it absorbs all colors in the white light except red. It transmits only red light. No green or blue light passes through.

If we use a blue filter, no red or green light passes.

If we use a filter of a complementary color, red-blue, it transmits red *and* blue light, but not green.

Next we use a yellow filter. It transmits red and green light, since it is a mixture of red and green.

Now let's combine two filters, so that we subtract twice. First a yellow filter. It transmits only red and green light.

Then we add a blue-green filter. It would transmit both blue and green, but there is no blue to transmit. It will not transmit red.

So the only light passing through is green.

By looking over the first four experiments you can work out many others. For example:

Two primary colors subtract *all* the light. The first filter is red, so only red light passes through. The red will be absorbed by either a blue or a green filter.

A primary color and its complement together subtract all the light.

If the first filter is red, a blue-green filter will cut off the red light transmitted. If the first filter is yellow, a blue filter will cut off the red and green light transmitted.

Gray is a mixture of white and black—light and darkness. If you hold a piece of white paper in sunlight, it looks white. At sundown it begins to look gray. On a dark night it will look dark gray or—if there is no light—as black as everything around it.

A colored object reflects the same *color* of light, as long as there is enough light to stimulate the cone cells of the eye. But the color becomes darker when less light is reflected.

If you have a scrap of colored cellophane, lay it on a sheet of white paper. Light passing through the cellophane is reflected back to your eye by the white paper.

Now place something gray under a part of the cellophane. It will not change the color, but it will absorb some of the light. The color looks darker.

The appearance of lightness and darkness depends, in part, on the brightness of surrounding objects.

Find a piece of some very light gray material. Cut it in half. Place one part on the white surface, the other on the black surface, a little distance apart.

Then call in a friend and ask him which of the two pieces is darker.

He is almost sure to say that the gray piece lying on the white surface is much darker.

There are many things around you which are called "white." Place some of them side by side for close comparison. You will find that some of them are much whiter than others.

So we know that colors are different wave lengths of visible light and that most of the colors we see are mixtures of different wave lengths.

How does the eye see colors?

We know that light falling on the light-sensitive cells causes a chemical reaction. We know that only the cone cells can distinguish different colors.

How? Does blue light cause one kind of chemical reaction, red another kind, both in the same cell?

Scientists believe that there are *three kinds* of cone cells. One type responds chiefly to red waves, another to green waves, the third to blue waves.

So, if we look at a blue-green object, only the blue-sensitive and green-sensitive cone cells respond. The red-sensitive cells do not.

How could the brain put together the messages from these cells, so that we see mixtures of colors?

Choose a printed color photograph in a magazine and

study it closely under a magnifying glass. You will see that it is made up of thousands of tiny dots.

The printer used only three colors of ink, together with black ink, in printing this photograph: yellow, reddish blue and bluish green. You will see places where the inks have mixed after printing, to form the primary colors (by subtraction).

In dark areas there are more and larger black dots. In light areas all of the dots are smaller, so more white light is reflected.

Now put away the magnifying glass and hold the picture at arm's length.

You see many colors—including many that are not really there! Your eye mixes them, by addition. The dots disappear, and you see all the gradations of color, light, and shadow which the printer intended.

Color is the eye's response to different wave lengths of light.

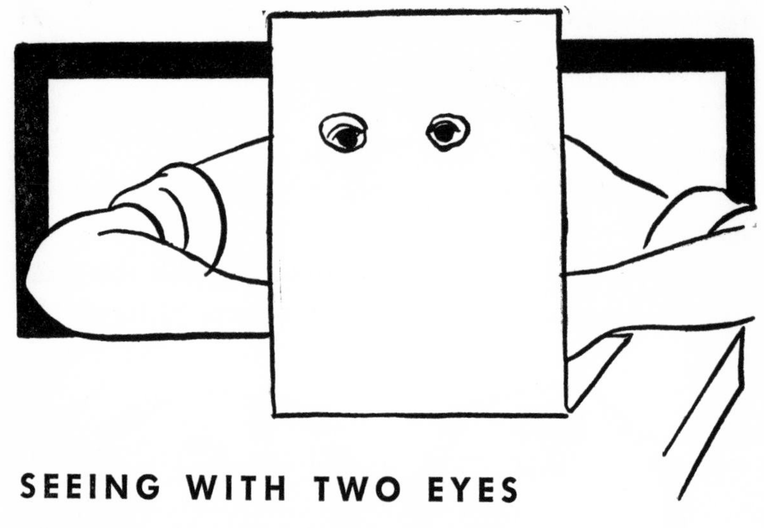

SEEING WITH TWO EYES

MEN AND other animals have two eyes.

Is one of them a spare?

Do both eyes see the same thing?

Why don't we see two images instead of one?

Let's make some experiments to discover what we see with two eyes. We see two pictures, and they are not the same.

Take a piece of stiff cardboard (the kind the laundry puts in shirts will do) and cut two holes in it. The holes should be about ¾ inch across and 2 inches apart. Fold the cardboard so that it will stand up on a table.

Stretch a string or draw an imaginary line across the table, beginning at a point midway between the two holes.

Place a small bottle, a saltcellar, or a toy soldier—something like that—1 foot from the cardboard, on the line. Place another 2 feet from the cardboard.

Close your left eye and look through the right-hand hole with your right eye.

Now look through the left-hand hole with the same eye, your right eye. You see two different pictures, like this:

Now look through the holes with both eyes at once. What do you see? The two pictures are put together in one.

Here is another experiment that reveals two pictures:

Place a can on the table, a round can with a printed label.

Look at it carefully, without moving your head. Look at it with your right eye, then your left eye.

Your right eye can see a little section on the right side of the can which your left cannot see. Your left sees a little section your right cannot see.

Yet with both eyes open, you see *both,* together. But do you really see two pictures when both eyes are open?

Hold up your right forefinger at arm's length. Hold up your left forefinger, in line with the right, about 10 or 12 inches from your nose.

Look at your right forefinger. Keep it in focus. The left forefinger is blurred—but you see two images of it.

Now look at your left forefinger. The right is blurred, but you see two images of it.

Did you notice that your right eye sees the closer forefinger to the *left* of the more distant one? Your left eye sees it to the *right.*

Focusing on the more distant forefinger, open and shut each eye rapidly, in turn. The nearer finger seems to jump back and forth.

Want to see a sausage?

Hold your two index fingers in front of your eyes so the finger tips meet in front of your nose. Focus your eyes on an object across the room.

Now move the finger tips apart a little. There's the "sausage," floating in mid-air!

Try it with your fingers about a foot from your eyes. Now you can make the sausage appear and disappear by focusing first on a distant object, then on your fingers.

What's the sausage made of?

Instead of your two fingers, use two pencils, of different bright colors, placing them end to end, then separating them. You'll see that the sausage is part one color, part the other, and mixed in the center.

Ask a friend to look at your finger while you hold it several feet in front of him.

Tell him to keep it in sharp focus. Move it slowly toward him. Watch his eyes.

See them turn inward? When the finger is very close, he looks cross-eyed.

This is called "convergence." To look at an object close to his nose, his eyes must converge, turn toward each other.

Two-eye vision—called *binocular* vision—helps us to judge distances.

Hold two sharpened pencils by their erasers, one in each hand.

Hold one not quite at arm's length, pointed upward.

Hold the other off to the side, horizontally.

Close one eye.

Now move the pencil from the side *quickly* toward the other. Try to make their points meet.

Try this experiment several times, first with one eye open, then with both eyes open.

This is not a test of vision alone, because you are using your muscles. Try it with both eyes shut! You will come close to making the pencil points meet, because you have muscular coordination: you can *feel* about where they are. But you will score more hits if both your eyes are open.

What happens? How do your two eyes help the brain to judge distance?

In geometry you learn to calculate the altitude of a triangle by measuring the base and the two adjacent angles. For example, here are two triangles. They have the same base. It is easy to see that the taller triangle has wider angles at the base.

The distance between your eyes is the base of a triangle; the apex of the triangle is the object you look at. If it is far away, your eyes converge only slightly, so the angles at the base are large. If it is close, they must turn in more sharply.

The angle of convergence is larger when you look at a distant object, smaller when you look at a near object.

Your seeing apparatus senses this change in angles. To look at a near object you must turn your eyes slightly inward. If you do this several times, you can feel the muscular change.

Binocular vision is helpful in many games.

Close one eye. Ask someone to toss a softball to you.

You'll probably catch it. But isn't your timing a little off?

See how much easier it is with both eyes open?

The fields of vision of your two eyes are not the same. We discovered this in experiments with peripheral vision.

Looking straight ahead, open and shut your eyes, one at a time, in turn.

Each sees a whole area which the other cannot see.

Why? One reason is that your nose is in the way!

Yet we usually seem to see one picture, not two. The seeing center of the brain puts them together.

Here is an experiment which shows how well the brain does it!

Roll a sheet of paper into a tube about one inch across.

Close your left eye. Hold the tube up to your right eye with your left hand, like this:

Now open your left eye.

You have a hole in your hand! With both eyes open, you seem to be looking right through it.

Here is another experiment:

Close one eye. Look at a small object across the room. Place the tip of one finger close enough to the open eye so that it blocks the view of that object.

Now open the closed eye. With both eyes open, your finger seems to disappear!

Have you ever looked through a stereopticon? The stereopticon was invented a hundred years ago, and your grandparents and great-grandparents may have collected stereopticon slides. Now they are becoming popular again, in smaller sizes and in color. There are several cameras on the market which take these "3-D" pictures.

When you look at a stereopticon or "3-D" picture, it seems real, because it has depth and roundness. Why?

A stereopticon camera is really two cameras; it has two lenses and makes two pictures at once.

The lenses are about as far apart as your eyes. Each "sees" a slightly different picture, just as your two eyes do.

When the pictures are developed, they are mounted

side by side and placed in a special viewer. When you look into the viewer, your right eye sees only the picture taken with the right-hand lens, your left eye only the picture taken by the left-hand lens.

Your brain puts the two images together, just as if you were looking at the original scene.

Each picture, looked at alone, would seem flat. The two together seem to have depth and roundness.

What does a one-eyed man see?

He is not severely handicapped. His field of view is not so wide, because his nose cuts off part of it. At first, when he loses the sight of one eye, things seem a little flat. But he soon forgets this, for he knows, by experience, which objects have roundness and depth.

His distance judgment is not quite as exact, perhaps. But while he loses the sense of convergence, the two eyes turning inward, there are other ways of judging distance.

For example, he can judge the relative sizes of objects. You do this too. For example, how large is this fish?

First cover the hand, so you see the fish and the man. Then cover the man, so you see the fish and the hand. It's a minnow or a whale, depending on how and where you see it!

If one object is behind another, you know it is farther away. So does a man with one eye.

Indeed, beyond a distance of 50 feet or so, the sense of convergence is of little help to two-eyed people in judging distances. We judge greater distances by the sizes of objects, textures, and perspective.

You can trick your vision and make an ordinary photograph look almost like a stereopticon picture with depth.

Choose a good sharp picture with objects in the foreground and clear background detail. A color photograph in a magazine is best.

Look at it with one eye shut.

All the objects look to your eye as they did to the eye of the camera.

If both eyes were open, you would know it is only a flat picture. Your eyes could not see a little way around each solid object.

But with one eye shut, this difference is hidden. It's easy to imagine that you are looking at a real scene, with depth, as the camera's eye did.

The next time you visit an art museum where the paintings of the old masters are on display, try looking at them with only one eye.

Many of these artists did all they could to give a feeling of perspective. You will have that feeling if you look at their paintings with one eye—as they hoped you would.

HOW FAST IS THE EYE?

By now you have a good idea of the mechanics of the eye.

You know how light is reflected from objects to the eye, how the lens bends it to form a sharp image on the retina.

You know that the rods and cones send nerve impulses to the brain, reporting the brightness and the kind of light that falls on them.

You know that the pupil opens in dim light, narrows in bright light. You know that the two eyes converge when they look at nearby objects, and that this action helps you to judge distance.

How fast is the eye? How quickly do all these things happen? If you see a flash of light, how much time elapses between the flash and *seeing* the flash? How quickly can you look from one spot to another?

The fastest action in seeing is the speed of the light that travels to your eyes. Moving at 186,000 miles per second, a flash of light could cross the United States six times while you blinked your eyes once!

The slowest action in seeing is adjustment of your eyes to the dark. The pupils adjust quickly. (You can see it happen in a mirror.) But the supply of visual purple builds up slowly.

When you enter a dark room, it takes five minutes or more before you feel your eye has adjusted. In a very dark room the supply continues to increase for half an hour or more.

Scientists test this by placing a person in a darkened room where there is one spot of white light. The light is dimmed until he can just see it. As his eyes become more sensitive, the spot can be dimmed still more. This continues for 30 to 45 minutes.

There are two reactions important in seeing. One is the *starting* of the reaction. Another is *stopping*.

If the reaction did not stop and start quickly, we would see many images, all mixed together, as our eyes moved about or as objects moved before our eyes.

As a matter of fact, we sometimes do see images mixed together:

Make a top, by cutting a circle, about 4 inches across, out of corrugated paperboard, the kind used in cartons. Paste white paper on one surface of the paperboard. Divide the white circle into segments, and blacken half of them with India ink or black pencil.

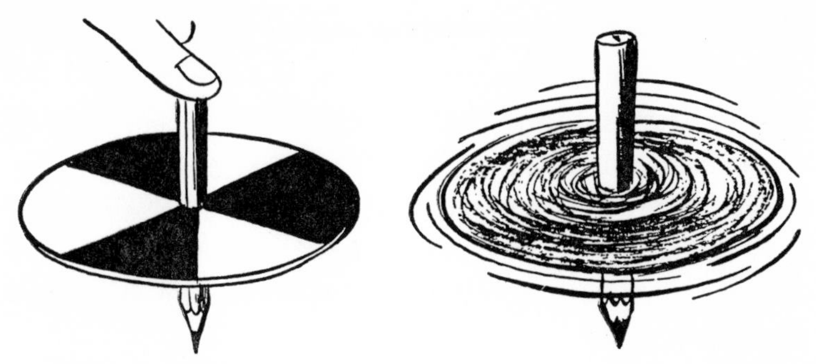

Sharpen a short pencil stub and push it through the center of the disk.

Now spin the top.

If you spin it rapidly, the black and white segments blend together in an even shade of gray.

The eye is not quick enough to see the black and white segments when the top spins at full speed. But as it slows down, they reappear.

The light reflected from the top doesn't get mixed up and become gray. A fast camera could take a picture of the spinning top and show the black and white segments.

But the chemical reaction in your retinal cells is not fast enough to make the stop-and-go change. A black segment comes into view before the image of a white segment dies away.

If you spin a spoked wheel, you see the spokes until the speed reaches a certain point. Then they blur. The chemical change in the cells cannot start and stop quickly enough to see them.

The contrast between bright and dim light affects the on-and-off speed of the cells.

When you look at an ordinary scene, there is no sharp contrast in brightness among the objects in view. In looking from the brightest to the darkest object, no cell must shift from a strong chemical action to little or none. A small change is enough, and it can make this change very quickly.

You can make an experiment to show what a difference contrast makes:

In daylight, ask a friend to point a lighted flashlight toward you and swing it around in slow circles.

Now repeat the experiment in a dark room.

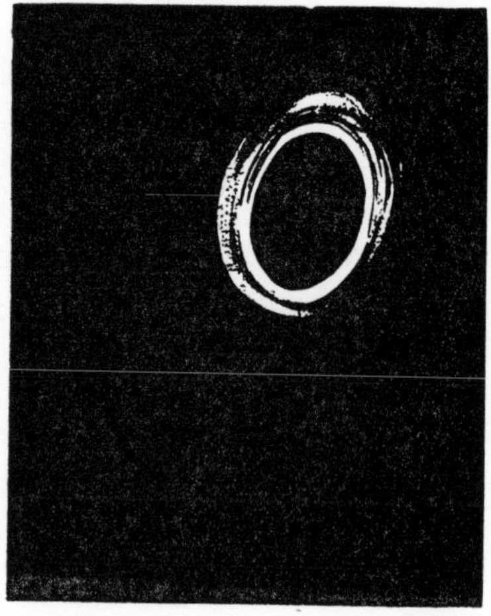

Outdoors there is no blur. In the dark room, the light leaves a long trail.

Outdoors the difference between the lighted flashlight and the surrounding scene is not great. The cells make the change quickly. It takes longer for them to change from the light of the flashlight to darkness.

To show a moving object, a cartoonist draws it like this:

He suggests a trail, like that of the flashlight. If you hold a pencil by one end and shake it back and forth, you will see a blur.

Why do we not see more blurred trails in the scenes around us, the motion of cars on the street, for example?

Suppose we photograph a fast-moving car with a camera. We set the shutter speed for 1/25 of a second. If the camera is held motionless while the car passes in front of it, the car will move 3 or 4 feet while the shutter is open. It will be blurred. But the background scene will not be blurred.

Now we take another picture. This time, as the car moves, we swing the camera to follow it. If we time the swing right, the image of the car will be motionless on the film when the shutter is open. In this picture the background will be blurred.

Put yourself in place of the camera. If you look at the background while the car passes, the car's image will be blurred. But, because your eyes are focused on the background, the car's image would be blurred even if it were not moving!

But if you turn your eyes to follow the car, the background will be blurred, both because of the motion and the fact that the background is in your field of peripheral vision.

Of course, if you photograph a moving object a long distance away, there is no blur, because its image moves only a tiny distance on the film while the shutter is open. You can see stationary and moving objects a long way off without blur for the same reason.

So we seldom notice this blurring, unless—as with the spokes—an object is moving too fast for our eyes to follow it.

Seeing something after its image has stopped falling on the retina is called *"persistence of vision."* It makes motion pictures possible.

You have probably seen a strip of motion-picture film. It is a series of still pictures, taken one after the other. If the object photographed is moving, each picture will be a little different from the one before it.

A motion-picture projector sends flashes of light to the screen. First one picture appears. Then the screen is darkened while the next picture is brought into place. Then comes another flash, throwing that picture on the screen.

If this were done slowly, you would see a series of pictures, one after the other. You would notice the changes, but the pictures would not seem to move.

But when this is done quickly, the image of one picture has not faded from your retina, the chemical change has not stopped, before the next picture appears.

How fast does this happen?

In a motion-picture theater, pictures are thrown on the screen at the rate of twenty-four per second. The screen is dark between flashes.

Silent film projectors, for home movies, are slower. Most of them show only sixteen pictures per second. (This saves film; you need less film to photograph a one-minute scene.)

Some projectors have a speed control, so they can be made to run even slower. If you have such a machine, you can make some experiments with the eye's speed.

In a dark room, turn on the projector, with no film in it. It will throw a white light on the screen.

If it is running at the rate of sixteen pictures per second, you may notice a little flickering.

Now turn down the speed control, slowly. The flickering will increase, as your eyes begin to see the dark periods on the screen.

When the projector is at its slowest speed, you can easily see the light and dark periods.

You can also demonstrate that brightness affects the eye's speed. Let daylight into the room, or turn on other lights. Repeat the experiment.

Now the flickering will be more apparent even at the projector's highest speed.

Persistence of vision helps to explain an old puzzle: Why do the stars twinkle?

They don't. *You* do.

The stars are so far away that light from a single star is a pin point, which would fall on a tiny cluster of cells, a group so small you can imagine it as a single cell. It would, that is, if you could stand absolutely still.

But you can't. There are tiny motions of your eye which you cannot control. The beating of your heart causes enough motion to move your body, and your eye.

So the pin point of light dances over group after group of cells, in quick succession. The fading image on each cell gives you the twinkling effect.

(By the way, did you know you could see many more stars by *not* looking at them? When you look directly at a star, its image falls on the center of the retina, where there are only cone cells. If you look a little to one side, its image falls on some of the rod cells, which are more sensitive to light. A star too dim to be seen with the cone cells can often be seen with the rods.)

There is another kind of afterimage which you may have noticed at times.

Stare at a bare, lighted electric light bulb for a few minutes.

Then look at a well-lighted white surface.

There is a dark spot at the center of your vision.

Why? The bright light exhausted the supply of the chemical substance that responds to light, but only where the image of the light bulb fell on the retina.

When you look at a white surface, all the other cells respond. The tired cells cannot. It takes a few minutes for the chemical balance to be restored.

You can see this exhaustion taking place.

Stare at the lighted bulb again. At first you see a very bright area around its center. As you continue looking, this area begins to fade.

What happens when you close your eyes after looking at a bright light? You see a bright spot.

The cells exposed to light are still active. They continue to report light to the seeing center of the brain. It isn't as bright an image as the real light, but it seems bright by contrast with the surrounding darkness.

You can carry this experiment further by using colored lights.

Stare at a bright red light. (It must be bright and not far from your eye.)

Now, when you look away at a white surface, you see a bluish-green afterimage.

Within the group of cells covered by the image of the red light, you have exhausted only those that report red. The others will respond to the light reflected from the white surface. White light minus red is bluish green.

Close your eyes. You see a red afterimage.

If you look at a bright green light, the afterimage on a white surface will be purple: white minus green.

This is not harmful to the eyes. The afterimages soon fade.

If you stare at bright lights for a long time, you might have headaches and your vision might be temporarily disturbed. But there would be no lasting damage.

But don't stare at the sun!

On a bright sunny day, take your magnifying glass outdoors.

Focus the image of the sun on a piece of paper.

When you do, you also focus the infrared heat rays. The paper scorches and may catch fire.

The lens of your eye also focuses infrared waves and ultraviolet waves (some of which cause sunburn). If you look at the sun, you are focusing a hot spot on your retina. You may burn the cells, leaving a permanent blind spot at the center of your vision.

Whenever there is an eclipse of the sun, newspapers warn people to look at it only through heavily smoked glass. Some foolish people pay no attention, and their doctors tell them they have "eclipse blindness."

Leaving aside the slow changes in the eye—getting used to darkness and the fading of afterimages—what can we say about its speed?

Light reflected to the eye travels almost instantaneously. Unless we are looking at the moon, the sun, planets, or the stars, the time is too short to matter.

The speed of the chemical change in the cells of the retina is slower, but still very rapid. How long it takes depends on the duration and brightness of the image.

For example, you can see a bright flash of light that lasts for less than 1/1,000 of a second—but its image will be seen for longer than that.

Aircraft observers are taught to identify planes by looking at their pictures as they are flashed on a screen. A picture can be recognized if it is flashed for 1/50 of a second.

The speed of the chemical change is so rapid that under everyday circumstances we can notice no time interval between *looking* and *seeing*.

Our eyes move very rapidly, by the way. Unless we are concentrating on some specific point, they seldom are motionless for more than 1/10 of a second. If we try to concentrate on a point, we may keep them almost motionless for one or two seconds, but then some involuntary motions begin. We can glance from one point to another in 1/50 of a second.

When the chemical change begins in a light-sensitive cell, how long does it take the nerve impulse to reach the brain?

Nerve impulses travel at better than 300 feet per second. This is much slower than the speed of light, slower than the speed of sound. But the distance from eye to brain is so short that the time lag is imperceptible.

A magician sometimes says, "The hand is quicker than the eye."

It isn't so. That's more of his "misdirection." The eye is very much quicker than the hand. And a rapid motion of the magician's hand would be sure to attract your eye and call attention to what he was doing.

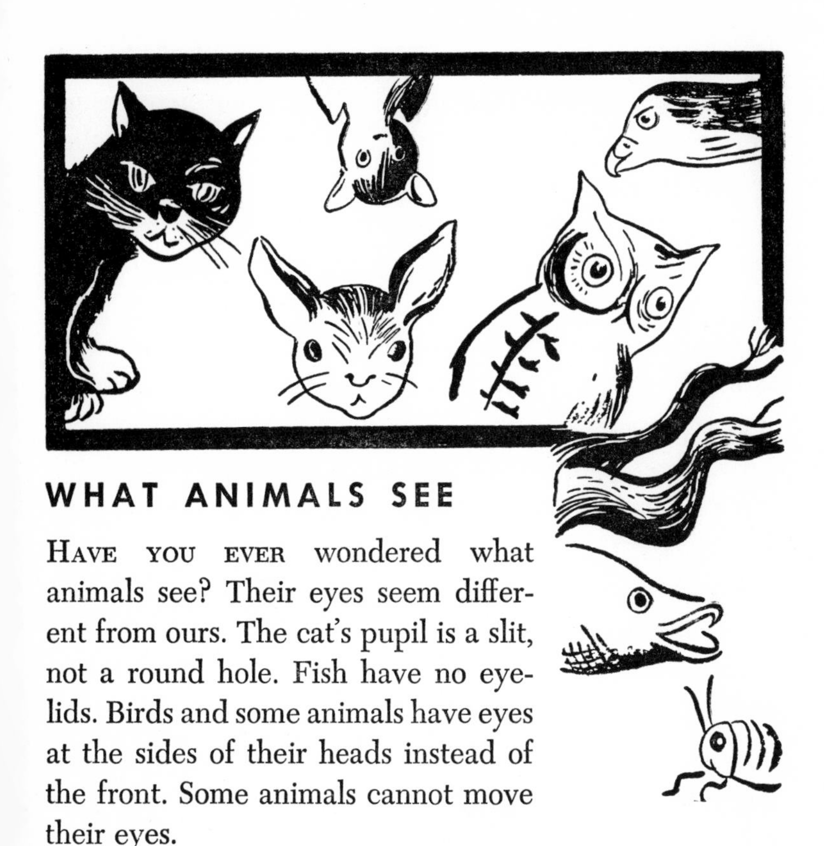

WHAT ANIMALS SEE

Have you ever wondered what animals see? Their eyes seem different from ours. The cat's pupil is a slit, not a round hole. Fish have no eyelids. Birds and some animals have eyes at the sides of their heads instead of the front. Some animals cannot move their eyes.

Of course a fish doesn't need eyelids to wash his eyes!

With his eyes at opposite sides of his head, the fish does not have our kind of binocular vision. He sees two separate fields, which overlap a little if at all.

Some fish can focus their eyes; some cannot. Those with focusing arrangements normally look at nearby objects; they can adjust them for more distant ones. But this adjustment is not always useful, because it is seldom possible to see very far under water.

Do fish see colors? We know very little about the color vision of fish. They do not see colors as we see them.

Divers with Aqualungs, exploring many feet below the surface, see little color. This is partly because there is too little light for their cone cells, partly because some colors in the sun's light have been absorbed by the water above.

But color photographs taken by artificial light show that there are amazingly rich, bright colors down there. Many fish are brilliant in color, though the color fades quickly when they are brought into the air.

Since a fish cannot close his eyes, can he sleep?

Eyes have very little to do with it. After all, we sleep with our ears open. Our eyes close in sleep because the muscles of our eyelids relax.

In the world of birds, some, like owls, are night fliers. Their retinas are made up almost entirely of rod cells. They have sensitive night vision; but they do not see colors, nor is their vision keen.

This is a good time to dispose of a false belief: that some animals can see in total darkness. Cats, owls, and night-traveling animals can see when there is only a little light. But there must be *some* light. Unless reflected light falls on light-sensitive cells, no animal can see.

Birds that fly mostly by day have retinas made up primarily of cone cells. Their vision is keen. They see colors—though not necessarily in the same way we see them. All we know is that some birds can distinguish between different colors.

Some of the day-flying birds have keener vision than ours. The tightly packed section of cone cells, the fovea, is better developed in their eyes.

There is only a tiny patch in our retinas where vision is keen enough for reading or seeing fine detail. The patch is much larger in the eyes of some birds. Their vision is keen over a larger field of view.

The patch in our eyes is roughly circular. Some birds have patches that form a broad band across the retina. If our eyes were so equipped, we could read off all the numbers on a motionless string of freight cars without moving our eyes.

A few birds have a strange arrangement. Each retina has two of these patches.

These birds—swallows, for example—have their eyes set well forward, so that the fields of view partially overlap. One pair of keen-vision patches is arranged so that they provide binocular vision of objects straight ahead. Thus they can judge distances with two eyes, much as we do.

The other pair of cone-cell patches gives sharp sideways vision. Thus the swallow can, at one time, look straight ahead, to the right, and to the left—and see details sharply in all three directions!

Bird eyes have a focusing arrangement, too. They can see distant objects somewhat better than we can. But they can also focus their eyes on objects an inch or two away: the insect or seed they are about to eat.

Writers who want to describe men as having keen vision call them "hawk-eyed." It is a good description. The hawk, soaring high in the air, can see small moving objects far below, objects we wouldn't notice.

What colors do birds see? They may see more than we do. We can see only seven colors in the spectrum of white light. We can distinguish perhaps two hundred different color mixtures.

Birds may see more than this. And they may see light outside the band of wave lengths that is visible to us.

We cannot imagine what the world would look like with such eyes. But we know it would be different.

For example, in past wars armies have used camouflage to hide things from aviators overhead. An airplane hangar, for instance, might be painted to resemble the surrounding woods. The painters would use colors which, to their eyes, seemed the same as the colors of leaves and bark.

Sometimes aerial photographers used ultraviolet sensitive film to photograph such places. Though the camouflage paint reflected visible light in the same way as the woods, it might not reflect the same amount of ultraviolet. When the pictures were developed, the airplane hangars or other buildings stood out sharply.

It is sometimes difficult to decide what animals see because they have other senses, too, including some that are strange to us.

How do migrating birds find their way over thousands of miles, returning to the same nesting places they used the year before? They seem to find their way over open water, above clouds, or even in dense fogs.

A homing pigeon may be carried far from his loft, in a closed coop, over country he has never seen from the air. Once released, he makes his way home again.

Bats rely not on their eyes but their ears, a built-in system like radar. Flying at night they make shrill squeaking noises too high-pitched (the sound waves too short) for human ears to hear. The echoes of these noises tell them where objects are and how far away.

People have stretched nets over the mouths of caves, leaving only a tiny opening, and bats, at night, have found the opening, flying through it without touching the net.

Dogs rely more on their sense of smell than on vision. They do not have a patch of close-packed cone cells. Their vision is fuzzy, and there is reason to believe they have little color sense.

Do you remember how, in your experiments with peripheral vision, it was easier to see an object to one side when it was moving? Dogs sometimes fail to see objects that aren't moving.

A dog may smell a rabbit but fail to see it until it moves. Many a cat has learned to sit quietly on a fence while a dog sniffs frantically to find it.

Dog trainers who use hand signals always use *moving* signals.

Many old dogs are almost blind. They see only enough light to avoid running into things. But their sense of smell is so keen that they can manage quite well. People often have difficulty deciding whether a dog is blind or not.

We focus our eyes by changing the shape of the lens. Animals have a number of different focusing arrangements.

The cat does not have a flexible lens. Focusing is not important at night, because seeing with the rods is fuzzy at best. By day the cat can sharpen the image on its retina by narrowing the pupil to a slit.

Here is an experiment with your own eyes to illustrate how the cat obtains a sharp image, in daytime, by narrowing its pupil:

Make a pinhole in a card.

Close one eye. Move a printed page closer and closer to the open eye until the type is too blurred to read.

Now, holding the book at this distance, look at it through the pinhole, holding the pinhole as close as possible to your eye.

The type is sharp enough to read.

Nothing changed in your eye when you looked through the card. But the pinhole had the same effect as narrowing your pupil to a pinhole.

If you can cut a narrow, short slit in the card with a very sharp knife, it will give you much the same result as a pinhole.

How do cats see so well in the dark?

First, they can enlarge their pupils more than we can, so their eyes gather more light.

Second, they have a special layer behind the cells of the retina, which increases the response of the light-sensitive cells. If you shine a light at a cat's eyes at night, while the cat is looking at you, you see a green glow, reflected from this green mirrorlike layer.

A CAT'S PUPIL CAN ENLARGE FROM A SLIT,

One of the oddest focusing arrangements is that of the horse. His eye has a slanting retina. One part is closer to the lens than the other.

Nearby objects are always in focus on the closer section of the retina, faraway objects on the other. To see a clear image of an object, the horse simply moves his eye so the image falls on the right area of the retina!

Is there any special usefulness, to an animal, in having eyes at the sides of the head?

Indeed there is. If you move quietly, you can sneak up behind a friend—or an enemy. He cannot see beyond the limits of his peripheral vision.

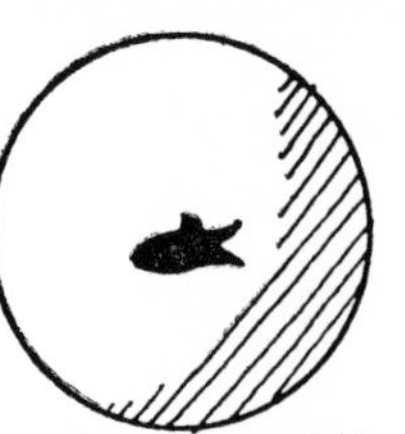

But you can't sneak up behind a rabbit! Rabbits, birds and other animals with eyes at the sides can see almost a full circle around them.

In a very general way, it might be said that side-set eyes are most useful to hunted animals. Forward-looking eyes that give good distance judgment are most useful to hunting animals. But there are exceptions to this rule.

By studying the eyes of animals, we can discover some of the differences in their vision. We know that some animals see better by day, some by night. Some have very keen vision, others rather poor. Some are color-blind; others can see colors. Some can see almost a full circle around them, but their fields of view do not overlap, as ours do.

In all animals, including man, vision is based on the same operating principle: that light, falling on light-sensitive cells, causes a chemical change, and that this chemical change causes nerve impulses.

SOME INSECTS' EYES ARE MADE UP OF THOUSANDS OF TINY FACETS

SEEING WITH THE BRAIN

IF YOUR optic nerves were cut, you would be blind. Blindness can also be caused by injury to the brain.

Youi eyes might be open, light falling on the retina, chemical changes taking place in the cells. But unless the nerve impulses reach the brain, and unless the brain understands them, you have no vision.

Our eyes gather visual impressions. The brain interprets them. And this interpretation is a surprising and fascinating process. Seeing is more than just looking.

Perhaps a hawk has better eyes than we do. But a hawk cannot read a book! Clear vision is useful. But much more important is the understanding of what the eyes report.

What do your eyes do when you look at a picture?

Scientists have a machine that traces the motions of the eyes. They go skipping and dancing, zigzagging back and forth, looking from one place to another. In a minute they may make more than a hundred motions.

Only a small part of each picture can be seen by the little patch of fine cone cells at one time.

But what does the brain see? You are not really aware of these rapid zigzags. Instead you build up a mental image of the whole picture, not the little pieces.

Much the same thing happens when you walk through the woods. You do not see the whole scene, even with your full peripheral vision. Your eyes dart back and forth. But in your mind is a feeling of space. You may step aside to avoid a puddle, though you are not looking at it, because your eyes reported it a few seconds before. You remember that it's there.

Memory is one of the brain's most important functions. Without memory, sight would be much less useful.

For example, what do these three signs mean to you?

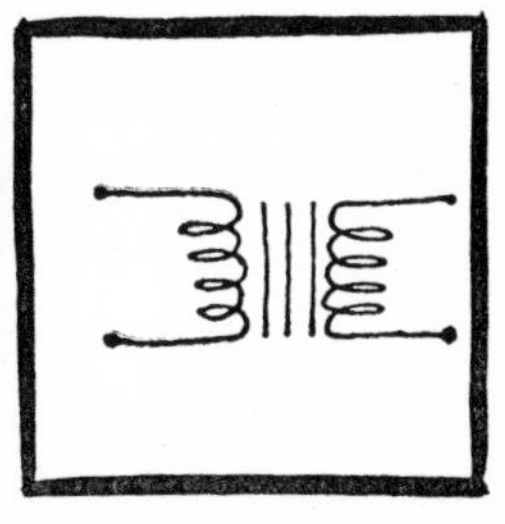

Perhaps as little as they would mean to a hawk! But you can learn their meaning and remember them.

The first one is used on weather maps. It means "west wind blowing at 13 to 18 miles per hour, with snow."

The second is a ship's signal flag. "I need assistance."

The third is used in electrical diagrams. It represents a transformer.

If you had not learned to read, this page of letters would have had as little meaning to you as those three signs. Your eyes could see the letters, but they would tell you nothing. When you learn to read, you learn to remember words and letters.

What is this?

A picture of a chair, of course. But how did you know? If you had never seen a chair, you would not have known. You recognize the drawing because you *remember* what a chair looks like.

As you look around you, almost everything you see is recognized by your brain. You have stored up in your memory the images of millions of objects.

These are not only visual memories. They are intertwined with all of your other memories.

Suppose you see the school you once attended. You recognize it. But the sight stirs other memories. Some are visual: a teacher's face, the playground at recess time. But you also remember things that happened. You may even remember the smell of the school corridors.

In the same way a memory may call forth a visual memory. A smell may remind you, with a mental picture, of the ocean or a flower.

Words call forth visual memories, too. For example:

Cat
Automobile
Meat

In reading each word you had a visual memory. But the mental pictures may have been fuzzy, because there are many kinds of cats, automobiles, and meat.

A skillful writer uses words to make your mental images more clear. And he calls up other sense-memories, too: smells, noises, touch sensations, and tastes. For example:

A big, playful, soft black cat
A rattling old Model T sedan
A thick, sizzling juicy steak

Each word makes the picture clearer.

The brain is very skillful at fitting observation and memory together.

For example, what are these?

You can answer without hesitation. One is an automobile. The other is a sailboat. These little pieces of drawings suggest mental pictures of familiar real objects.

Because of memory, you often seem to see more than you actually do! For example, what is this?

A pencil and a glove.

But is it? It *could* be two short pencils, just possibly. But the brain sees it as one pencil.

What is this?

Three men? It could be two and one-half. The man at the rear might be cut off at the waist. But that isn't very likely. The brain sees three men.

Look around you and see how many of the objects in view are partially hidden by others. It would be confusing, indeed, if you saw each of them as part-objects, if you considered the possibility that the parts you can't see aren't really there!

How good an observer are you? Some people are much better than others.

How many dots are there in each of these groups?

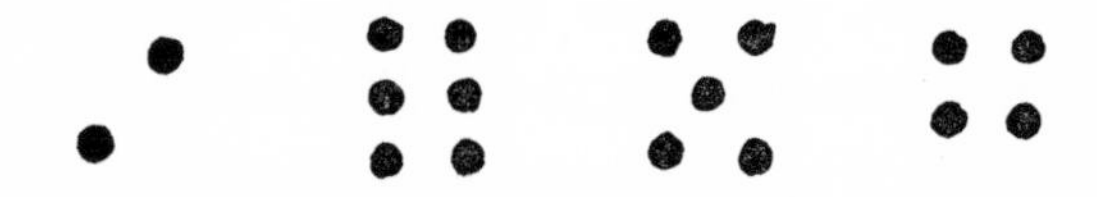

When you were five years old, you would have counted the dots one by one. Now you have played so many dice games that you recognize the patterns at a glance, without counting.

How many dots are there in these groups?

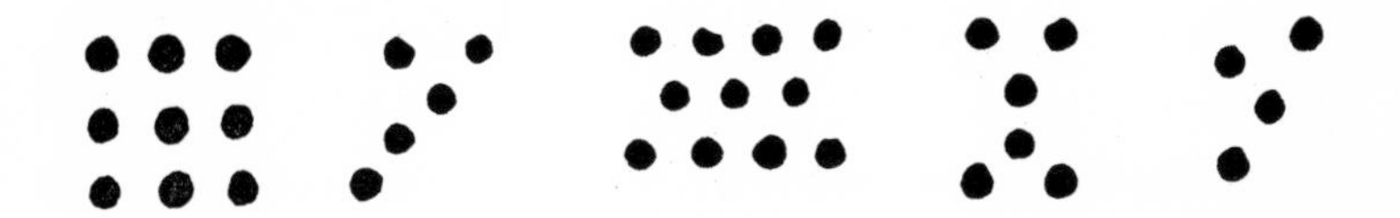

This time you had to look more closely and count the dots, one by one or in groups. The patterns are not familiar.

But you could train yourself to remember them, to recognize them as quickly as the patterns on dice.

Indeed, if you practiced for some time you could learn to "count" much larger numbers of objects at a glance. You would not count the exact number; you would *estimate.*

A stockman can glance over a large plain, on which some of his cattle look as small as ants, and say: "There are 6,000 head." In fact, there may be 5,947 or 6,066. But 6,000 is a good working figure. It might take all day to count them one by one.

Estimating is a useful ability. Many people can estimate the weight of a piece of meat or a fish, just by looking at it—and be correct to within an ounce. People can estimate numbers, height, area, the speed of motion.

A man who had never seen and weighed a piece of

meat could not estimate as well. A good estimator is using his visual memory, remembering something he has seen in the past which closely resembles the one before his eyes.

When you counted the dots in the unfamiliar patterns, how did you do it?

Some people look at the dots while they count them.

Others can glance at the patterns, then look away and count them from memory. They "photograph" the patterns before knowing how many dots there are.

This may seem to be an unusual ability, but we all do it.

Ask someone to arrange a few pennies, nickels, dimes, and quarters in an irregular group and cover them with a sheet of paper.

Get ready to look. Tell him to whisk away the paper and replace it, giving you just a brief glimpse.

How many coins were there? How many of each value? What was the total amount of money?

Didn't you take a mental photograph? As you answer each question, don't you "look" at that mental image?

Can you develop your powers of observation? Here is a game to play with your friends. Any number can play. You can test your own ability. And, by playing it a number of times, you can see whether your ability is improving.

The scorekeeper should place a number of objects on a table. (If only two are playing, you can take turns playing and scoring.)

Begin with fifteen or twenty objects: a coin, a match folder, a spoon, a key, a cup, an ashtray, and so on. The scorekeeper covers them with a newspaper.

At the word "Go!" he removes the newspaper. The players have five seconds to look at them. Then he covers them again, and each player writes a list of all the objects he can remember seeing.

Each item he lists correctly counts one point. Take off two points for wrong guesses.

You can increase or decrease the number of objects or the time allowed for looking, to make the game more fun.

In this game, you know in advance what you will be asked to remember. Now try another game. In this the questions will be unexpected.

This game will work best with at least five players. Form two teams, with the odd man acting as judge and scorekeeper.

The members of team A and the scorekeeper leave the room. They arrange to perform a little play, without spoken words. The scorekeeper prepares a list of ten questions which the members of team B will try to answer.

The scorekeeper comes back. At his signal the members of team A enter the room, perform their little play, then leave. The play should last not more than three minutes.

Now the members of team B *turn around* and face the other end of the room. The scorekeeper asks questions about what they saw, and they try to answer. Unless you want to keep individual scores, let the team members decide together on each answer; there will be some fine arguments!

The trick in this game lies in the kinds of questions asked. They should be unexpected questions. For example:

"What color was Bill's necktie?" (He wasn't wearing one.)

"Was there anything unusual about his clothes?" (He was wearing one black shoe, one brown one.)

"What did Jim take out of his pocket?" (He picked up a notebook and put it into his pocket. He took nothing out. Correct answer: Nothing.)

"Who came into the room first? Who went out first?"

"What object was on the seat of the chair?" (This is a tough one, because no one touched it or called attention to it in the play. It was just there.)

This game of observation is often played in real situations. The police are often exasperated because witnesses to a crime tell such conflicting stories. Here are the statements made by several bank employees describing a bank robbery:

"There were two men."

"No, there were four."
"They wore black masks."
"No, they had no masks on."
"They were all clean-shaven."
"No, one had a mustache."
"They all had pistols."
"No, one of them had a shotgun."

Seeing, remembering what things are, holding mental pictures in your memory, is one of the brain's jobs.

Another is interpreting what you see, reading meaning into it. Here the brain uses memories of past experiences. It fits together memory and observation by *reasoning*.

For example, an expert tracker can study the ashes of a campfire, the marks in the soft earth, and other signs and reconstruct a picture of what happened hours before:

"Three men with four horses camped here last night. One man was a prisoner. One of the others was tall, and one was short and fat. The short man caught fish for supper. They had flapjacks, bacon, and coffee for breakfast."

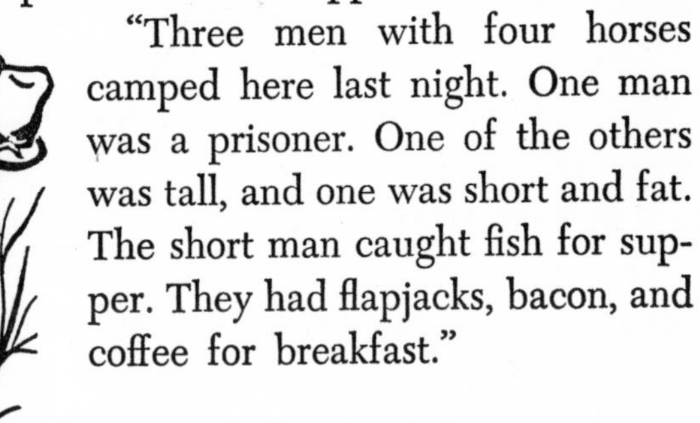

The brain will use all of the information it can, not just visual information.

Its method of memory searching is one of the great puzzles of science. Your brain is, in a way, a vast filing cabinet, full of scraps of information accumulated ever since you were born, important and unimportant. Only a tiny fraction of this is information you have *decided* to remember.

Because of the higgledy-piggledy way we gather information and because of the fact that so much of what we remember seems almost accidental, the brain would seem to be a very disorderly filing cabinet—millions of scraps of information tossed in without organization or plan. We can't take out memories and inspect them, or do much tidying up.

Yet somehow we can reach into this huge, disorderly pile and pull out what is, usually, the right information!

If we let our thoughts wander, they will run through a strange sequence of memories. You can begin anywhere. Fix your thoughts on a pencil, a thumbnail, a spot on the wall. Close your eyes, relax, and the long chain of memories begins to appear.

The most powerful associations are usually visual, but other senses are closely related—as you can sometimes observe when they come into conflict.

PICTURES AND ILLUSIONS

In an earlier chapter we discussed vision and balance. A tightrope walker needs both senses.

Some amusement parks have a "crazy room." You reach it by walking through a dark tunnel and opening a door, which closes behind you.

It is an ordinary room, with doors, windows, furniture, and pictures on the wall. But the room is tipped at an angle. The furniture is fixed to the floor and the pictures to the walls.

Most people, when they enter this room, go slipping and sliding down to the low end. They feel dizzy, sometimes a little sick.

Their eyes tell them it's an ordinary room and that they should stand up in the usual way, parallel to the walls. But their sense of balance tells them this is all wrong.

A few people can remain calm. They can refuse to accept what their eyes and memories tell them and behave in accordance with their sense of balance. They can walk about on the slanting floor, stand without falling.

But most people are more influenced by their sight than their sense of balance. They try to stand up—and slip or fall.

There are all kinds of sense memories. We don't have to *be* off balance to feel that way.

For example, look at these pictures:

Don't they make you feel a little uncomfortable? They are well drawn, but they aren't *right*. The boy would fall off the seat in that position. The book would fall off the table.

What about this one?

The objects in this picture have the right relationship to each other, but not to *you*.

We can be made uncomfortable by other things that look impossible or unlikely.

For example:

This suggests a heavy mass resting on a slender support, probably too weak to hold it. It makes us a little uneasy.

What about this? There's nothing wrong with it. But most people will dislike the illustration. It seems wasteful to use such a heavy column to support a light weight.

In these examples, we are at the border line of art appreciation. Some of these principles are used by artists, architects and interior decorators—by all people who work in the visual arts—to make their creations attractive. They know that visual impressions are closely linked to both visual and other sense memories.

For example, here is how a classical architect used marble columns:

What if he had done it this way?

Here is one wall of a room. There is nothing impossible about the arrangement. But we dislike it. It seems out of balance.

Suppose we want to frame a picture. The first way?
No, that looks top-heavy. What about the next?
It's still not quite *right.* The last way?
That's better!

Most people find certain shapes pleasing, others less attractive.

Framed the first way, the picture seems to sag, as if it had slipped down.

In the second drawing, the margins are equal. It isn't pleasing.

The third way shows the picture with a little more margin at the bottom. It seems to be in better balance, and this is the way pictures are usually framed.

We like some regularity in our shapes. We like rhythm. For example, a carpenter could build a door like this:

But who would want it?

This border pattern is disturbing.

This one contains the same figures, but they are arranged in rhythm.

But in many pictures we "see" things that aren't there. This, too, the artist must recognize.

For example, this picture is not attractive:

Why? The important thing in the picture, the center of interest is the girl. But instead of being near the center of the picture, she's up in a corner.

This isn't the way our eyes would look at a real scene. We would focus her image at the center of our vision, where it would be surrounded by our peripheral field of view.

But here is the same girl in the same place in the picture—and it looks right.

Why? Because she is diving from a tower. The center of interest is where she will be an instant from now. By drawing the picture this way, the artist has suggested *action.*

If you block off all but a little square around the girl, you will see how much of the feeling of action is lost.

The artist has made us look where we *would* look if the scene were real.

Study the full-page advertisements in a magazine. Notice how they make use of balance, how the artists who planned them have arranged things so that your eye is directed to the things they want you to see.

The brain does more than receive impressions from the eyes, of course. In following the experiments in this book, your brain has given orders to your eye muscles: "Open. Close. Look this way. Look that way." And your eyes have done as they were told.

By giving such orders, you can open and shut your eyes, move them, focus on near or distant objects.

Usually, however, these orders are given by a part of the nervous system which is automatic. We don't have to decide, each time, to look here or there.

If an object flies toward our eyes, we blink automatically, before we are consciously aware of seeing it.

And we cannot control, by conscious thought, the opening and closing of the pupil, the chemical change in the light-sensitive cells, or the speed of adjusting the eye to darkness.

Indeed, even the muscles we control consciously are not fully under our control. We cannot turn one eye up while the other turns down. We cannot focus one eye for a distant object while the other looks at a nearby object.

It's a good thing, too, that we can't! There is an old story about a centipede who tried to think about what each one of his many legs was doing. He got himself into a terrible tangle!

Let's play some tricks on our vision.

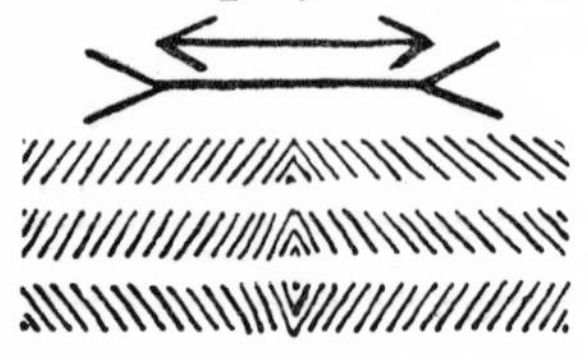

Which of these lines is longer? They're both the same.

Which of these lines are straight, which ones curved?

Use the edge of a piece of paper to be sure.

Here are two pieces of jigsaw puzzle. Which is larger?

They're exactly the same, in size and shape.

Here are two small circles, each inside a larger one. Which of the small ones is smaller?

Again, they're the same size.

There are many such optical illusions. Here are some others. If you look at each of them closely, you will see the picture change before your eyes.

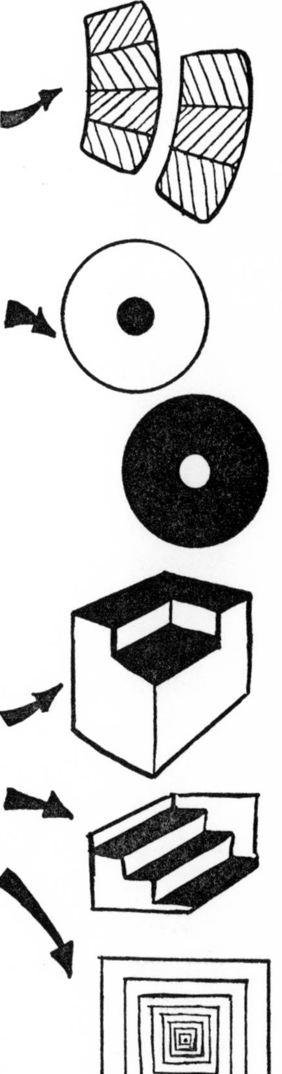

This looks like a box with a chunk cut out—or three walls with a small box in the corner.

These steps are right side up—or upside down.

Here you look down a long corridor—or at the top of a pyramid.

Have you ever seen a full moon rise? On the horizon it looks enormous. But if you could measure the image, you would find it no larger than that of the moon later on, high in the sky.

There are illusions of motion, color, shape, size. Now we come to one which isn't exactly an illusion.

Which man is taller?

If the three figures were standing side by side, with no surrounding objects, you would say at once that they were all the same size. In the picture the man on the left *seems* taller.

And, if this is a picture drawn from life, he *is* taller. The picture shows him to be farther away than the man at the right.

It might seem at first that your brain isn't very intelligent to be fooled by these illusions. But, in fact, it takes an intelligent and educated brain to be "fooled" in this way.

Were it not for this intelligence and training, we could not see meaning in photographs and drawings. They would be just collections of dark and light spots and splashes.

A savage cannot see meaning in a drawing, when he sees one for the first time.

Let's see how an artist draws a box. If he looked at a box face on, he might see it like this:

But that is not, to our eyes, a box. It might be a box—or a sheet of paper.

He must suggest depth, by showing us the top and sides. So he turns the box a little to one side and looks at it from above.

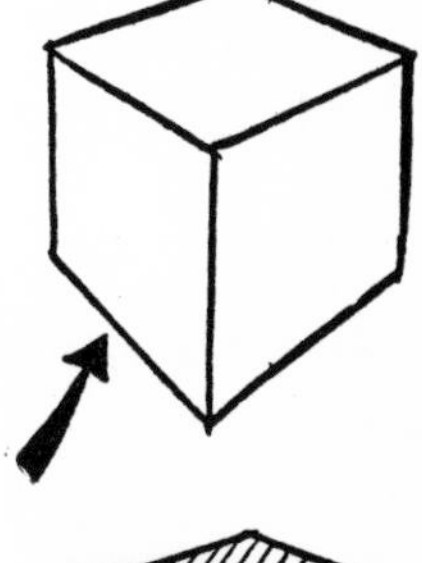

That's better. But it still doesn't look quite like a box. When we look at a real box, we see reflected light. Light usually comes from one main source. One side of the box will be brightly lighted, reflecting the most light. Another may reflect less, and a third be in shadow. So to show us that the box is real, the artist must show light and dark sides.

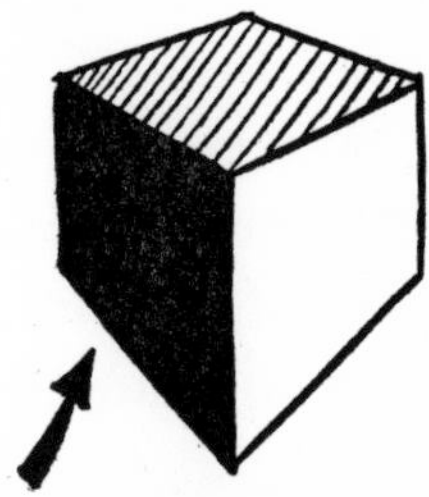

Now, where is the box? Floating in mid-air? If it were resting on a surface, it would cast a shadow, like this.

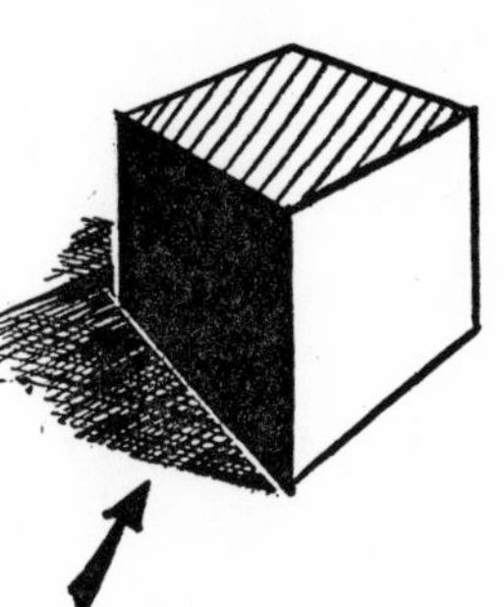

How big is it? How far away is it? The artist can answer *both* questions by answering *either*.

He can put something next to the box which has a familiar size, like this:

This suggests another improvement in the drawing: perspective.

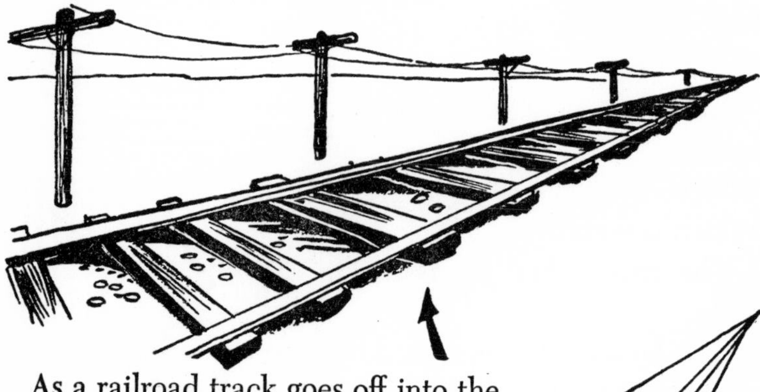

As a railroad track goes off into the distance, it looks like this:

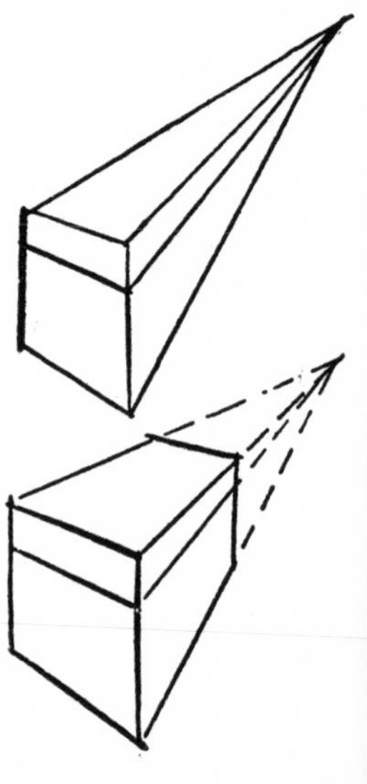

So, if our box were as long as the railroad track, it would be drawn like this:

Since it is not, the artist chops off the proper length, like this, the rear edge now being a little shorter than the front:

Now we have a box that looks right. But it is still only an illusion. It is nothing more than some ink marks on a flat sheet of paper, not a real box.

What would happen if the artist got mixed up and showed light falling in two directions, wrong perspective, and so on?

Let's see some other illusions before we go on to another subject. Which of these shapes is taller? Which is wider?

The stripes fool us. Both are the same.

This kind of illusion is used by dress designers to flatter their customers.

Dress designers, in fact, use many illusions to fool the eye. Here are necklines designed to make long necks look shorter or short necks look longer:

But sometimes a dress designer has a customer who is just plain shapeless. Stripes and necklines won't help much. So—what's the answer?

Camouflage! A design that so bewilders the eye that the body shape is hardly noticed.

TAKING CARE OF YOUR EYES

Even before you read this book, you knew how important vision is in your life. We all have some fear of blindness. But most people have some false ideas about blindness.

What causes blindness?

If there were no light, we could not see.

If our eyes were shut, light could not reach the cornea.

If the cornea, the liquid lens, the lens, or the jellylike vitreous were not transparent, light could not reach the retina.

If the cornea or the lens were removed, light would reach the retina, but it would not be focused to form an image.

If the cells of the retina were damaged or diseased, they would not generate the messages to the brain.

If the optic nerve were blocked, the messages could not reach the brain.

If the seeing center of the brain were damaged, it could not receive and understand the messages.

Serious injury or disease can cause total blindness at any of these points.

A few people are born blind. Their eye mechanisms did not develop properly. Some babies, usually those prematurely born, lose their sight.

More than half of the totally blind people in the United States lost their vision after the age of fifty, usually because of diseases related to aging.

Younger adults and children sometimes lose their sight because of disease. It is not always disease that begins or has its center in the eyes. The eyes can be seriously affected by illnesses centered elsewhere in the body, as well as by lack of proper food or vitamins.

In many cases, blindness through disease can be prevented, or at least checked. But the disease must be detected early and treated by a competent physician. Far too often it is not.

Why?

First of all, many people have the mistaken idea that "glasses" are the proper remedy for any eye disease. This is as silly as thinking crutches are a cure for broken legs. Eyeglasses with properly ground lenses will bend light; that is all they will do. If the lenses of the eyes cannot bend the light to form a sharp image on the retina, glasses may help. They will not cure an eye disease.

Glasses are necessary for many people, who could not

see clearly or comfortably without them. But they must be the right kind of glasses.

In Chapter 2, we mentioned two eye conditions that, if severe, require corrective glasses: nearsightedness and farsightedness.

Another common condition is *"astigmatism."* The cornea is not quite spherical. In some eyes, the curve is a little too sharp, or the curve is greater in one direction than another, like the surface of one side of an egg.

If the difference is marked, vision is slightly distorted. Astigmatism, too, can be corrected by proper lenses.

There are a few other conditions, also, that call for eyeglasses. In many cases there is a combination of problems: the individual is, for example, both farsighted and astigmatic. Further, the two eyes may not be quite alike. Each needs a specially prescribed lens.

Believe it or not, there are some stores that sell eyeglasses without a prescription! The customer tries on one pair after another until he finds one that seems suitable.

He will very likely choose the wrong kind, almost surely not the lenses a doctor would prescribe. What is worse, he may postpone discovery of a serious eye condition.

The second reason that some people do not obtain prompt medical diagnosis and treatment is this: They do not know how to find an eye specialist. There is much misunderstanding and confusion about such terms as "optician," "optometrist," "oculist," "ophthalmologist."

If you will look in the classified telephone directory,

you will find a heading, "Opticians." These are individuals or companies that grind lenses and sell eyeglasses on prescription. If an eye doctor gives you a prescription for glasses, you will take it to an optician to have it filled. Opticians often make and sell other optical devices: telescopes, binoculars, perhaps microscopes.

Following this section in the Classified is the heading, "Optometrists." You will find here some of the same names as under "Opticians," perhaps with slight changes. For example, under "Opticians" you may find the John Smith Company. Under "Optometrists" is Dr. John Smith, of the same address.

John Smith is a doctor—of optometry. He is not a physician and has not attended medical school. He has been trained to examine eyes for such disorders as nearsightedness, farsightedness, and astigmatism and to prescribe eyeglasses.

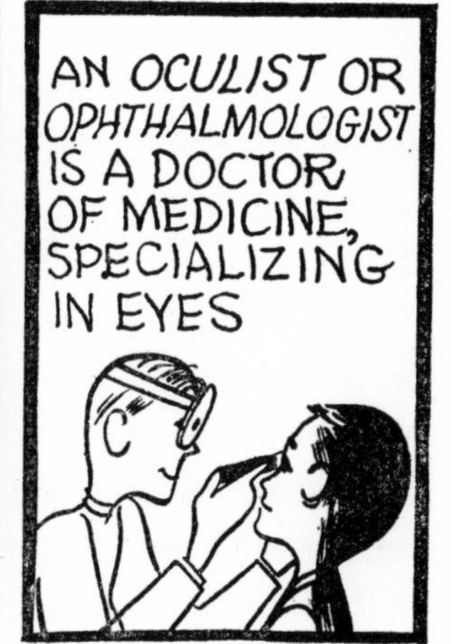

Because he is not a physician, he is not professionally qualified to diagnose many kinds of eye diseases, or diseases centered elsewhere in the body which affect the eyes. He cannot prescribe medicines or perform surgical operations.

The eye specialist, usually called an oculist or ophthalmologist, does not have a special listing in the Classified. He is a physician, and his name appears in the directory under "Physicians." His office may be marked only "John Jones, M.D."

Dr. Jones has qualified as a medical man, and can practice medicine. He has had additional training as a specialist in disorders of the eye.

How can you find an eye specialist? There are three good ways:

1. Ask your family doctor.
2. Call the local medical society. It is usually listed under the name of your town or city ("Newark Medical Society").
3. Call a local hospital.

When should you see an eye specialist?

Of course you should go to an eye specialist whenever you suspect there may be anything out of the ordinary about your eyes: pain, headaches, difficulty in focusing—any apparent change.

Every child should have a thorough eye examination before entering school.

Many doctors suggest that it is advisable to have your eyes examined at regular intervals, just as you have your teeth examined.

Accidents cause some children and adults to lose their vision.

Many eye diseases can be cured or checked. Some eye injuries can be healed or repaired. But it is all too easy for a stone, arrow, dart, BB, or firecracker to inflict damage that cannot be mended.

The eye tries to protect itself by blinking. But a tiny object may not be seen, or a larger one not seen in time. The eyelid is not thick or tough enough to protect the eye against a sharp arrow or a flying stone.

Taking chances with your vision, or a friend's, is not common sense. Tossing a handful of sand or gravel at someone can be more dangerous than throwing a sharp knife!

What about objects in the eye?

Often the wind will blow a bit of grit into your eye. It is painful. The eye fills with tears, and you have an almost irresistible desire to rub it.

The tears may wash the grit to the corner of the eye. You may help them along by using an eyecup, or plunging your face into a basin of water and opening the eye.

If this doesn't help matters, grasp the eyelashes of the upper eyelid and draw it gently down and over the lower lid; release it slowly, so that the lower lid wipes the inside of the upper.

Still there?

We're getting on dangerous territory now. Any further steps require a deft person with clean hands and a freshly laundered handkerchief.

He can pull down the lower lid. If the grit is in plain sight, lying in the red trough beneath the eye, he may pick it up with the corner of the handkerchief. If he sees the grit lying on the *white* portion of the eyeball, he may try to remove it by touching it very gently with the tip of the handkerchief corner.

That's all he should do!

If the grit is still there, go to a doctor promptly.

The danger of these bits of grit is that they may become embedded and cause infection. That's why rubbing is dangerous; it may embed a piece of grit which was loose and ready to wash away.

Never allow anyone but a doctor to try removing a speck of dirt from the cornea.

Most large factories have several cases like this each day. They record them as "foreign body in eye" accidents. They have nurses on duty. But while the nurses treat ordinary cuts and scrapes and give first aid in more serious cases, they are usually forbidden to touch an employee's eyes. The man with grit in his eye is sent to an eye specialist.

So if that annoying grit is still in your eye, go to a doctor. Some people think the proper place to go is a drugstore, but a druggist is no more an eye specialist than is a locomotive engineer or a tailor.

How do you find a doctor in a hurry?

1. Go to the nearest hospital or clinic. They treat many cases like this every day.
2. Go to a nearby doctor, or your family doctor. He will look at the eye and decide whether he can take care of it. If the grit is deeply embedded or embedded in the cornea, he will almost certainly send you at once to an eye specialist who has the equipment to examine and remove it.
3. Of course, if you know of an eye specialist, go directly to him.

Suppose you are at the beach or in the woods, a long way from a doctor?

If first-aid measures don't work, close the eye and keep it closed with a soft pad of cotton, gauze, or a handkerchief. Hold the pad gently in place with a handkerchief, shoelace, or bandage tied around your head. Use only enough pressure to keep the eyelid shut. And get to the doctor as quickly as you can.

What about general care of the eyes?

For example, should you wear sunglasses?

The answer is "Yes"—if you are a mountain climber, an aviator flying at high altitudes, a prospector out in the desert, or a sailor in the South Seas.

Visible light will not damage the eyes, even though it is very bright. But too much ultraviolet light will sunburn the surface of the corneas, as it sunburns your skin.

Manufacturers of sun lamps, which give off ultraviolet light, warn their customers to cover their eyes or wear sunglasses while lying under them. A few people ignore this warning, because the visible light does not seem bright; they sunburn their corneas, which is very painful.

Good sunglasses cut off some of the ultraviolet light. Since you cannot tell by looking through them how much protection they provide, you should have expert advice. But there are very few places on earth where there is enough ultraviolet light to make this protection necessary.

What if you are walking along a white, sandy beach on

a bright day, skiing, or driving a car with the sun in your face? When the visible light is uncomfortable and dazzling, there is no objection to wearing sunglasses.

Good glasses have optically ground lenses; cheap ones distort the image and may cause a headache. If you wear eyeglasses, an optician can duplicate your eyeglass prescription with tinted lenses.

It is not a good idea to wear sunglasses unless you are really made uncomfortable by bright light. People who wear them on the street—or even indoors!—may lower their eyes' tolerance to light.

This might be an advantage—if you had a special kind of task which required good night vision. If you had to drive a truck every night, wearing sunglasses on bright days would improve your ability to see after dark.

But most of us are more concerned with good daytime vision. So, unless your eye specialist advises it, wear sunglasses only when you really need them to be comfortable, not to be "fashionable."

Should you wash your eyes with eye lotion?

Not unless your eye specialist advises it and prescribes a lotion.

The eye makes its own lotion, and the lids wash the eye several times each minute. Artificial lotions may interfere with this process and irritate the eye.

Can you damage your eyes by using them too much?

Not if you have normal eyes. In fact, the reverse is true; you can impair vision, at least temporarily, by not using them.

A few children are born with eyes that point in different directions, so they see two images, not one. This can often be cured by an operation, but until then one eye is covered with a patch. Vision in that eye may have been normal; but after a period of disuse its vision is poor. So, after the operation, the other eye is covered for part of each day to force the first to get back to work.

Scientists who use microscopes use their eyes alternately. They aren't afraid of tiring the eye that looks through the microscope, but of impairing the one that isn't in use.

If you are farsighted and do not wear glasses, doing a lot of reading or close-up work may tire the ciliary muscle. If your eyes feel tired or you have a headache after close focusing, have your eyes examined. Glasses may help.

Trying to read or work under too dim a light, or in a glaring light, may make you uncomfortable or headachy. It won't damage your eyes. Aside from the discomfort, you won't read or work as well. In factories it has been found that improvements in lighting greatly increase production and reduce mistakes.

What is a good light?

That is not a simple question!

Let's consider reading. What happens when you read this page?

Light is reflected from the white surface, most of the visible light. The black type absorbs light. What you see is the white page, not the black letters.

If there is too little light, the white surface will appear gray. Less light will reach the light-sensitive cells, and reading becomes more difficult.

A 75-watt bulb about 6 feet from the page will provide enough light.

Some kinds of paper, especially those on which magazines are printed, have a shiny surface. Some black inks, too, have a shiny film. A bright light falling on a shiny surface will be reflected, as by a mirror.

If you hold a shiny page close to a light at the right angle, you can see a reflected image of the light, just as you would in a mirror.

Since bright lights, and bright spots, are dazzling, you do not want a reading light that is too bright, nor should it be placed so that a bright spot is reflected from the page to your eyes.

This is enough to describe the proper light on the pages you are reading: a light bright enough to reflect a white image from the page, but without glare or "hot spots." It should be placed so that no shadows fall across the pages.

But your eyes see more than the pages. Peripheral vision must be considered, too.

Suppose your reading light were the only light in the room, and it had a metal shade.

The page of the book would be well lighted. But everything else in the room would be dark. The white page would stand out in sharp contrast. The cells receiving the white image would adjust to the light; the cells receiving no light from the surrounding area would try to adjust to darkness.

The pupil and the cells tend to adjust to the total amount of light reflected to the retina. A candle flame looks very bright in a dark room, but pale yellow next to a bright light.

Thus you will read better if the room is well lighted. In addition to the reading light, there should be lights that provide general illumination.

These other lights should be so arranged that there is no bare bulb or bright spot within your peripheral vision as you read. Ceiling fixtures, wall fixtures, shaded or indirect lamps—these are good. It is annoying to have a bridge lamp across the room so placed that the bare bulb is within your field of view.

No doubt you have been told that your reading light should come over your left shoulder. Why?

Most people hold books a little to the left. The left hand supports the book, the right turns the pages. If the light came over the right shoulder, the head might throw a shadow on the page, and the right hand would cast a shadow when it turned a page.

What about reading in bed?

The real problem is that you read instead of sleep!

It will not harm your eyes if you sit up, hold the book squarely in front of you, and have a good light.

If you read lying down or on your side, you may hold the book at an angle, one part of the page farther from the eyes than another part. This can be tiring.

What about television? Is it harmful to the eyes?

In answering this question, we are talking only about eyes in good condition. They have been examined by an eye specialist, who found no disease and no need for glasses (or he prescribed glasses).

What happens when you look at a television screen?

Unless you sit very close (where the picture isn't as good), you can see the entire screen without moving your eyes. The screen is an almost flat surface, and your eyes hold the same focal distance while looking at it, as well as the same convergence.

What happens?

Hold your forefinger close to your nose, as close as you can hold it with the image in clear focus. The eyes are converging almost as much as they can.

Hold this position, without moving your eyes, for several minutes.

When you look away again, it will be something of a

relief. The muscles feel some strain holding the eyes converged and motionless.

In this respect, television is unlike motion pictures. Watching television, your eyes converge at, perhaps, 8 or 10 feet. Watching the movies in a theater there is much less convergence; the screen may be 50 feet away, or more.

Holding any position with any muscle of the body for a long period of time can cause some discomfort. In ordinary daily activity, the eyes are in constant motion, the muscles in constant use. Even in reading the eyes are constantly moving.

Doctors are not in agreement that harm can result from this. But it would be surprising if it did not cause temporary discomfort and visual difficulty.

Common sense suggests one precaution: Don't stare at the screen hour after hour. Take a break after each program. During the breaks, turn up the room lights, use your eyes. Even during the program, don't keep your eyes glued to the screen; look away for a few seconds now and then.

As in reading, avoid too much contrast. Keep some lights in the room, so the screen is not surrounded by blackness.

WHAT IT'S LIKE TO BE BLIND

MANY PEOPLE have serious visual handicaps but are not totally blind. Sighted people cannot easily imagine what total blindness is like. Unless they understand the machinery of vision, it is even more difficult for them to imagine what a partially blind person sees.

Suppose, for example, the cone cells at the center of vision do not function. With this kind of handicap a person sees everything *except* the object he looks at! He is aware of objects around him, of motion, and, to some extent, color. His night vision may be good. But he cannot see details. He cannot read. He could not easily use a screw driver.

What if these cells are intact but the cells away from the center of vision are not functioning? This person would see the world as if through a long tube or tunnel. In fact, this handicap is called "tunnel vision." He can read and do fine work, but he bumps into things when he walks across a room.

What if the cornea, liquid lens, lens, or vitreous should become cloudy? This would reduce the amount of light reaching the retina, and blur the image. The person could see shapes and outlines in good light, but he would be blind at dusk.

Have you read about "eye banks"? Doctors cannot replace an entire eye. But they have succeeded, in some cases, in replacing a portion of a cloudy or damaged cornea.

This is a delicate grafting operation. A tiny section of the faulty cornea is removed. It is replaced with a section of clear cornea obtained from a donor. Donors are not easy to find, of course. But occasionally, for example, a cornea may be donated by someone who is hopelessly blind from some other cause but has healthy corneas.

This kind of surgery has restored sight to many people. But it is helpful only when blindness or severe handicap is caused by a cloudy or damaged cornea. And the operation is not always successful; the new section may soon become cloudy.

Have you heard of an eye disease called "cataracts"? It frightens some people, but all it means is that the lens of the eye loses some of its transparency.

This may happen in just a few spots, and it may not even be noticed.

Why? Repeat your experiment with the light bulb and magnifying glass. Make some spots on the lens with India ink or electrician's tape or heavy grease pencil. The spots do not appear on the image. You simply cut off some of the light and make the image a little dimmer.

Cataracts may cover much of the lens without causing blindness. But when they become severe, vision may be seriously impaired.

Many years ago "doctors" performed a rough-and-ready operation for cataract, simply knocking the lens out of place. This allowed light to reach the retina, but it was not focused into an image.

More recently, in severe cases, it has been the practice to remove the lens surgically, then give the patient thick glasses to bend the light. This restored vision, but without the focusing variations of the lens. Vision was clear at only one distance.

A British physician has had considerable success using a plastic lens to replace the eye's own lens. It will be several years before doctors can be sure how well these plastic lenses work.

Some people are color-blind.

They may see as well as anyone, except that they cannot recognize and separate certain colors.

Most of them are not wholly color-blind; they do not see the world in shades of gray. They see some colors. But some that we see look alike to them.

Unfortunately the colors most often confused are red and green, the colors that mean STOP and GO to automobile drivers. Once it was felt that such people could not safely

drive cars. Today, in some places, they are allowed to, because most states and cities have traffic lights with the red signal at the top.

What is color blindness?

There are three types of cone cells, each especially sensitive to one color of light.

Partially color-blind people have only two types of cells that respond; their color sense is limited to mixtures of two colors.

Totally color-blind people have only one type of cell responding. They are sensitive only to variations of shade.

Color blindness is generally considered incurable. But it is more annoying than serious.

Total blindness is a serious handicap indeed. Learning how to live as a blind person takes hard work and study, as well as courage. The sooner a blind person begins his studies, the easier it is for him.

People who lose their sight sometimes refuse to give up hope of seeing again. They refuse to believe that their vision will not return, no matter what the doctor says. Unfortunately, some doctors are unwilling to tell their patients the unhappy truth.

Of course blindness may sometimes be cured, or partial vision regained. There are also a very few cases of blindness which cannot be helped medically, but where some accident restores partial vision.

But a competent eye specialist is unlikely to make a mistake. As you can see by studying the seeing apparatus (page 33), some kinds of disease or damage could not possibly be repaired. It is frightening to be blinded, but hope and confidence begin to return when the blind person begins to learn new ways of doing things.

If blindness comes on gradually, he should begin his special training before vision is totally lost. It will be easier then, and the final loss of sight will be less frightening.

An untrained blind person cannot walk across a room. He fears loss of balance, stumbles, loses his way, gropes aimlessly.

He cannot dress himself, match shoes and socks, choose a tie, shave, put toothpaste on his brush. At the dinner table he has difficulty finding his food—and sometimes his mouth!

He is afraid of noises, feeling defenseless.

Indeed, in the early days of blindness the ordinary problems of day-to-day living—dressing, washing, eating—become so great that he has little thought for more ambitious undertakings.

But watch a trained, adjusted blind man!

He is traveling alone, by plane. Getting off, he places his finger tips on the elbow of a fellow passenger and follows him easily down the steps and into the airport. A porter collects his bags and leads him to a taxi.

He pays the taxi fare; one-, five-, and ten-dollar bills

are in separate compartments of his wallet, and he recognizes coins by touch.

He signs the register at a hotel, and the bellboy's elbow guides him to his room. He memorizes the number of steps from the elevator and the turns in the corridor; next time he can find the room alone.

In his room, the bellboy shows him the closet, window, bathroom, the outlet for his electric razor. The light switch, too, for many blind people prefer to have the lights on after dark, even though they cannot see them.

When he leaves the room, he uses his white cane.

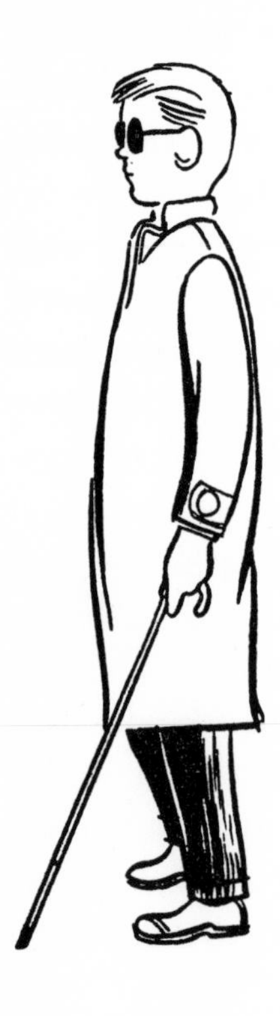

This cane is much more than a walking stick. It is longer, so that it touches the ground a step and a half ahead. He swings it from side to side, feeling steps, obstructions, and rough spots.

Some blind people develop a sense something like a bat's, though not as keen. By hearing the taps of their canes, noises of other kinds, and echoes, they build up a mental picture of objects around them. A few can walk quite rapidly, avoiding pillars and posts without touching them.

The white cane is also a portable traffic sign. In all but two states, the law requires that all traffic stop at the sign of a raised white cane.

The traveling blind man, stopping in a hotel, finds his own way back to the lobby. A bellboy guides him to the restaurant.

The waiter reads the menu to him. He orders and may ask that his meat be cut in the kitchen. He locates his glass and the salt and pepper. Few other diners would know he is blind.

After dinner he uses a lighter to light his cigarette. He snaps open the case of his special wrist watch and reads the time by touching the hands.

Since this is a business trip, he has asked the hotel to hire a secretary for him. Next morning the secretary reads his mail, as well as the newspaper, and accompanies him on his calls. Perhaps that afternoon the secretary is busy typing, and he makes his calls alone.

Visiting friends that evening, he plays bridge with them, using cards with Braille symbols. Or he may join a group of blind men at a bowling alley, where they have a special rail to guide their approach.

He has learned to read and write Braille. This is a system of raised dots, read by finger tip:

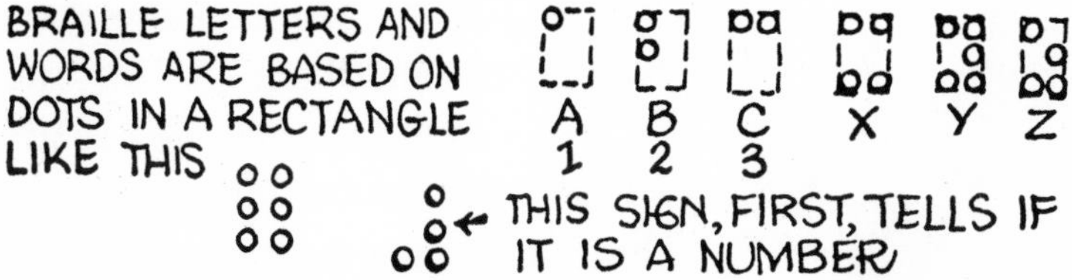

BRAILLE LETTERS AND WORDS ARE BASED ON DOTS IN A RECTANGLE LIKE THIS

A B C X Y Z
1 2 3

THIS SIGN, FIRST, TELLS IF IT IS A NUMBER

He carries a small Braille typewriter, and the names and addresses of his business friends are jotted down in Braille. But he relies on his memory more than most of us.

He can obtain books and a few magazines printed in Braille. But Braille is not a very satisfactory substitute for visual reading. It is much slower—as if you read this page by speaking each individual letter aloud. And Braille books are cumbersome. If this book were printed in Braille it would have nine times as many pages (or three times as many, three times as large) and it would weigh more than twenty times as much.

He enjoys Talking Books more. These are books read aloud on phonograph records. He can borrow albums of these records through the public library.

He listens to the radio in his hotel room to hear the day's news.

At home, he sometimes plays golf. The caddie lines him up for long shots, describes the fairway and the distance. When he putts, the caddie taps the pin in the cup to guide him.

In the summer, he likes to swim.

He has a Seeing Eye dog.

The dog is trained to lead him, avoiding obstacles, even overhanging branches, and crossing intersections with the green light.

It's bad manners for strangers to pet the dog; he has a job to do.

The dog is a good companion, and he prefers to walk with the dog in his home town. With the dog he strolls in the park or along the river.

But the dog is less helpful when he travels. Feeding and walking him is a problem, and the dog is not a guide in a strange town. So he leaves the dog home when he goes on a business trip.

Where are blind persons trained?

Many states have special schools for blind children.

Some parents think it is better to have a blind child attend a regular school. This seems to have good points. But in the early grades, a blind child misses too much unless he has the specially trained teachers and the special equipment a school for the blind provides.

There he can study with the help of models. In geometry, for example, pegs, strings, and other devices are essential. He will learn to read Braille. The teachers will show him many little tricks and short cuts which help in daily life.

With this solid foundation, he may later go to a regular high school or college. Few children who do not go to special schools in their early years are able to succeed in college later.

Adults who lose their sight will find special schools and training centers in many states and most large cities. Most of them are operated or supported by Federal or state agencies, or aided by local community chests.

You may hear the term "vocational rehabilitation." It means "job training." The blind adult is trained either to return to the type of work he did before or to perform a new kind of work.

Is a member of your family blind, or have you a blind friend?

Many people are a little uncomfortable when they meet a blind man. They don't know what to do.

There are a few simple rules of courtesy. If you remember them, you can get along easily with any blind person, and help him, too.

1. Blindness doesn't make him deaf or stupid. But many people talk to a blind man as if he were a small child, or they shout! Just talk to him as you would to anyone his age.

2. When you walk with him, let him touch your elbow. Never grab his. You will walk a half step ahead of him. Hesitate just a little before stepping up or down.

3. Don't hesitate to use words like "see" or "blind." Most blind people say, "I'm glad to see you."

4. Speak when you enter the room. He wants to know who is with him.

5. If you sit next to him at the dinner table, tell him where the food is on his plate. Pretend it's a clock. "Your meat is at nine o'clock, potatoes at two o'clock, peas at five o'clock." Tell him what is on the table (bread, butter,

celery), and guide his hand to his water glass. When you pass a plate to him, tell him you're doing so, then just touch it to his fingers. Ask if he would like to have you cut his meat.

6. He might run into a door that's left ajar. Keep an eye out for toys on the floor or projecting lamp shades.

7. When you guide him into a room, lead him to a chair and stop. He'll run his hand over it and sit down. If he smokes guide his hand to the ashtray.

8. Whenever you have time, offer to read to him. Almost every blind person depends on readers. He'll have plenty of reading he would welcome: newspapers, books, letters.

9. Ask questions about blindness if you wish. He won't be offended or hurt. But blindness is an old story to him. He has as many other interests as you do. And he depends on conversation for much of his information about the world.

Many blind young people have been successful in high school and college because of the help offered by their sighted fellow students. Usually a group of students offers to share the responsibility of reading lessons to them, writing for them, and assisting in other ways.

MORE ABOUT VISION

This is the end of the book, but it could be—for you—the beginning. The study of vision is a lively science indeed. Many scientists today are studying vision, seeking answers to the remaining mysteries, seeking better ways of using vision.

Because eyes are so important to us, because we use them every minute that we are awake, it is surprising how little the average person knows about vision. If you remember much of what is in this book, you know more than most adults.

Even so, there are many questions this book has not answered. And there are some it could not answer, because science does not yet know the answers.

"When I look at the sky, I see bits of stuff floating. Is this dirt in my eyes? Can I get rid of it?"

No, it isn't dirt, and you can't get rid of it. Before you were born, the vitreous of your eye was full of blood vessels. Later they shriveled and disappeared. The floaters are the remains of these blood vessels. They are normal and harmless.

"Are people right-eyed, the way they are right-handed?"

Yes, most people have a "master eye." Here is how you can find yours.

With both eyes open, look at an object across the room. Bring up your finger quickly to eye level and point it like a rifle at the object, still looking at the object with both eyes.

Hold the finger steady. Now, first with one eye and then the other, sight along the finger. If you are right-eyed, you will find that you have automatically lined up the finger between your right eye and the object.

Some experts with the shotgun shoot with both eyes open. Perhaps without realizing it, they sight along the barrel with their master eye.

"If I lose one eye, will I go blind in the other, too?" Here's an old story. What truth is in it?

1. Blindness may have been caused by a disease which affected both eyes, one sooner than the other.
2. Both eyes may have been damaged in an accident. One was blinded immediately. The other became infected or did not heal properly.

But it is simply not true that the remaining eye would be damaged by "doing too much work." If the eye is healthy and undamaged, it will serve its owner as well and as long as any normal eye.

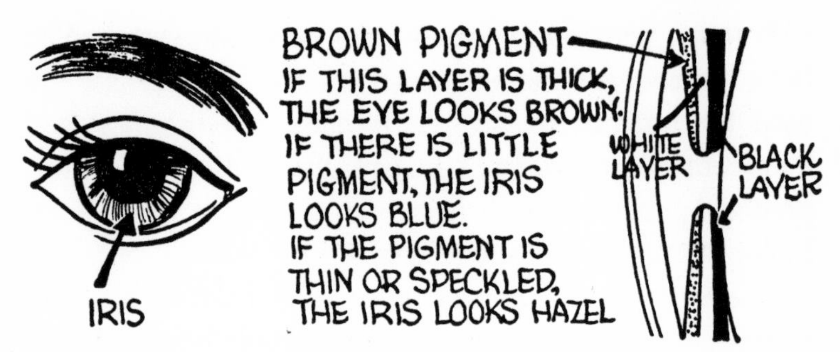

"Why are my eyes blue? Why are some eyes brown or some eyes green?"

The color of the iris depends on color absorption and reflection. The iris has several layers.

Farthest back is the lining of the eye, almost black. Above it are some small, irregular blood vessels, sheathed in white.

Next comes a layer of brown pigment. Blue-eyed people have almost no pigment here, so light is reflected from the two deeper layers. If the brown layer is thin or speckled, the iris will show the combined colors of the upper and lower layers and look greenish, hazel. If the brown layer is thick, it will not transmit much light to the lower layers, and the reflected light will be brown.

One of the challenging and interesting problems in human vision is that it does not fall within the boundaries of any single branch of science. In this book we have drawn upon the work of oculists, neurologists, chemists, physicists, psychologists, artists, and other specialists.

For that reason this book could be, for you, the introduction to many other subjects.

Perhaps you found lenses especially interesting. You have learned the basic principle of the lens. Lenses are used in cameras, telescopes, transits, microscopes, and many other instruments. Lenses are used by astronomers, photographers, research scientists, surveyors, navigators, biologists, and other specialists.

There are many experiments you can make with lenses, which can be bought from scientific supply houses. Many amateur astronomers build their own telescopes. You can make a simple microscope. You can build your own photographic enlarger.

In another chapter you learned some of the first steps in drawing. These principles are used by artists, draftsmen, architects, and designers.

Color is a big subject. Color specialists are needed in the printing, paper, and textile industries. Color knowledge is used in decorating, sales promotion, dress designing. More and more commercial products are "color-styled" to appeal to consumers.

Today there are color engineers, people who understand how our eyes and brains respond to color.

In hot weather, a room will seem cooler if the walls are a light gray-blue. It will seem warmer if the walls are of a color containing red.

Red is exciting, blue soothing. If a restaurant uses red liberally in its decorations, the customers will eat in a hurry. If soft blues and greens are used, they will relax, eat more slowly.

Accidents in factories have been reduced by color engineers. Dangerous moving parts and obstructions are painted in a bright color, contrasting with floors, walls, and the bodies of the machines. Steps are painted to make them more visible. Fire stations in factories are painted bright red, so they can be seen quickly by someone looking for an extinguisher.

Vision is a vitally important matter in flying airplanes and in flight-control operations. The United States Air Force and the air forces of other countries have sponsored much research in vision.

For example, when England was being attacked from the air in World War II, control centers were set up to plot the air defense. As quickly as enemy planes were sighted, information was flashed to the control center. The enemy planes were spotted on big maps: their location, direction, speed and altitude, and what types of planes they were. Controllers studied these maps and issued orders to the defending plane squadrons.

It was essential that plotters, controllers and others in

the control center be able to *see* all of the details on the big maps.

That sounds easy, but it wasn't. Scientists had to do a great deal of research work to decide how big the maps should be, what sizes, shapes, and colors of movable markers should be used on the maps, and where the spotters and controllers should sit.

For example, they found that many mistakes were made when arrow markers shaped like this were used:

But few mistakes were made when they used this shape:

As a specialist in vision, you might become a doctor, artist, architect, photographer, psychologist, physicist, chemist, biologist, television cameraman, motion-picture director, landscape architect, stage designer, engineer, magazine editor, printer, map maker, textile dyer—any of several dozen specialties.

But whatever you do in life, you will use your eyes. How well you use your eyes will make a great difference in your accuracy, speed, and skill.

Quick, accurate observation is useful to woodsmen, reporters, detectives, airplane pilots, baseball players, railroad engineers, salesmen, army officers, sailors, traffic policemen, lawyers—in fact, to almost everyone.

In everyday living, quick and accurate observation can save your life.

Suppose you are driving a car down a highway. If your powers of observation are below average, you will be aware of the car ahead of you, the one approaching from the other direction, the traffic light ahead, and the cars entering from side streets.

If your observation is quick and keen, you'll also be aware of several cars behind you, including one edging out to pass. You'll be watching several cars ahead. You'll see a little piece of fender behind an approaching truck and know there is a car that might pull out of line.

But you will also be aware of things you can't see!

When a ball rolls into the street, you'll slam on your brakes—because you know there may be a child running after it.

And you'll be aware of things that *may* happen. If you see a dog and his master on opposite sides of the road ahead, you'll slow down, realizing that the dog, at any instant, may run toward his master.

Most of us take vision for granted. Only a blind man can fully appreciate what vision means.

But we can, by understanding our eyes, protect them better. Even more, we can learn how to use them better, how to use them in exploring the limitless, spectacular wonders of the world around us that only vision can reveal.

INDEX

About the Author and Artist

JOHN PERRY has lived in Washington, D.C., since 1939, but his work has taken him through much of the United States. As a consultant on visual presentation and human relations, he has worked with industries, associations, professional societies, Federal agencies. One of his long-term clients is the National Federation of the Blind.

In 1946–1947 he was editor for *Federal Science Progress*. He has contributed articles on physical and social sciences to many magazines, and is the author of a recent book, *Human Relations in Small Industry*. He has been a lecturer at the American University and the University of Maryland.

JEANNE BENDICK is known everywhere in the children's-book field for her ability to explain and illustrate difficult concepts in a simple graphic way. She has illustrated many science books and has written and illustrated *All Around You, How Much and How Many, Television Works Like This,* and *Electronics for Young People*. A native New Yorker, she lives with her husband and two children in Great Neck, Long Island, New York.